SCHOLASTIC

ACTIVE™ English 7
Literature Reader

Name: ______________________________

Class: ______________________________

This edition specially created for Scholastic India.

First edition 2012
Reprinted 2012 (twice), 2014 (thrice), 2015, 2016, 2017, 2018, 2019, 2022

ISBN 978-81-8477-736-9

Contents

 ISBN 978-81-8477-736-9

1 The Six Fools

Retold by Anupa Lal

The Emperor was tired. He had been conversing with scholars for several hours.

"My head is heavy, Birbal," he said. "I wish to lighten it."

"A few days of riding and hunting will refresh Your Majesty," said Birbal.

"Why not try a different amusement?" asked Akbar. "Do you realise that as an emperor I converse only with wise men? Find me the six most foolish men. It seems ages since I had a hearty laugh! Six days to find the six greatest fools in Agra. Not too daunting a task for a man of your intelligence?"

Birbal hid a smile. "No, Your Majesty. Fools are never in short supply."

But Birbal soon discovered he was wrong. No one he met seemed foolish enough. Five days passed and the last day of his search dawned. Once again Birbal set off from home.

Birbal stopped to pluck a flower from a bush on the roadside when a man came running backwards and banged into him.

"Forgive me, *huzoor*," said the man. "I did not see you. I am a muezzin. I call devotees for prayer in the mosque nearby."

"But why are you running backwards?" enquired Birbal.

"I am running with my voice," said the muezzin earnestly. "I wish to see how far it carries."

Birbal was delighted! He had found his first fool! He said, "The Emperor will be happy to meet such a dedicated man. Come to the court tomorrow."

Birbal continued on his way. He then saw a man on a donkey, holding a bundle of firewood high above his head.

"Your arms will get tired, rest your bundle on the back of your donkey," said Birbal.

"The poor creature is already burdened by my weight," said the man. "I cannot increase his burden."

"That is indeed a generous thought," said Birbal. He had found his second fool! "Come to the court tomorrow. The Emperor will be happy to meet a noble soul like you," added Birbal.

The afternoon sun was blazing. Feeling thirsty, he walked towards a well in a

 ISBN 978-81-8477-736-

nearby field and saw a man digging. From the piles of freshly dug-up earth, it seemed as if the man was digging up the entire field!

Birbal walked over to the man.

"It seems you are searching for something," said Birbal.

"*Ji huzoor*," said the man. Sweat streamed down his face. "I buried a bag full of gold coins in this field eight months ago. But I can't find it."

"Surely you marked the spot where you buried your money?" asked Birbal.

"I am not a fool," said the man. "Of course, I did. There was a big, black cloud in the sky, shaped like an elephant. I buried my bag under it. I don't know where the cloud has gone, but I"ll find my money even if I have to dig up the entire field!"

Birbal's eye gleamed! He had found his third fool! "Our Emperor will be happy to reward a hardworking man like you. Come to the court tomorrow."

Night had fallen by the time Birbal turned homewards. He had discovered only three fools. A frown creased his forehead.

It was a bright, moonlit night. Birbal had almost reached home when on a stretch of open ground he saw a man examining the ground.

Birbal stopped. "Can I help you?"

"I am looking for my ring, *huzoor*." He straightened up to ease his aching back. "I dropped it under that tree." He pointed to a peepal tree nearby.

 ISBN 978-81-8477-736-9

Birbal was startled. “If you dropped it there, why look for it here?”

“There is light here,” said the man. “There is no light there.”

Birbal smiled. “Come to the court tomorrow. Our Emperor enjoys meeting intelligent men like you.”

The following day, Birbal presented all four fools. Akbar listened with a straight face as Birbal related how he had met each one. All four were richly rewarded.

Akbar's eyes were twinkling. “These men are indeed four of the most precious fools in our kingdom! But I asked you for six.”

“*Jahanpanah*,” said Birbal, “please count me as the fifth fool.”

Akbar raised his eyebrows.

Birbal continued, “For having devoted so much time and energy to this search.”

“Hmmm!” said the Emperor. “And the sixth fool?”

Birbal bowed his head. There was pin-drop silence in court. Then, Akbar burst out laughing.

“Your Emperor is the sixth fool, is he not?” said Akbar. “For sending you on a wild goose chase?

“All this foolishness has refreshed me!” said Akbar with a broad smile. “Thank you, Birbal! Now, let us attend to the matters of the state...”

 ISBN 978-81-8477-736-9

Understanding the meaning

scholar
A **scholar** is a person who specialises in a particular branch of study.

daunting
A task is **daunting** when it seems very tough to do.

dawned
A new day **dawns** when the sun rises in the sky.

muezzin
A **muezzin** is a person who calls fellow Muslims for prayer in the mosque.

PRACTICE

A Find a word in the passage that means the same as each of these words.

exhausted	________	kind	________
intelligent	________	prize	________
sincerely	________	investigating	________
devoted	________	alarmed	________

B Choose the best answer for each question.

1 The king was tired. He wanted to lighten his ____________.
(a) treasury
(b) head
(c) garden
(d) robes

2 What did Akbar want Birbal to find?
(a) six of the bravest men in the city.
(b) six of the most foolish men in the city.
(c) six of the most attractive men in the city.
(d) six of the most intelligent men in the city.

 ISBN 978-81-8477-736-9

3 Birbal said, "Fools are never in short ____________."
   (a) clothes
   (b) kingdoms
   (c) supply
   (d) gardens

4 Why was the muezzin running backwards?
   (a) He wanted to see how far his voice would carry.
   (b) He wanted to see if he had the ability to run backwards.
   (c) He was ordered by the king to do so.
   (d) He wanted to see how fast he could reach home, running backwards.

C Read the text and answer the following questions.

1 Why did Akbar want to lighten his mood?
2 Why did Birbal call the second fool a man with "generous thought"?
3 Where had the third fool buried his bag full of money?
4 Why did Birbal list the king as the sixth fool?
5 List the fools that Birbal found at the end of his search.

D Answer the following questions.

1 Who was the sixth and final fool in Birbal's list? How did he fit the criteria?
2 How is Birbal and the king's relationship a unique one?

E If you were Akbar and wanted to lighten your mood, what activities would you have done to ease your mind? Answer in 150 words.

 ISBN 978-81-8477-736-9

2 Rats' Whiskers

By Leslee Lazar

Not all animals have well-developed hands like humans. For instance, the rat's paws are small, they cannot move their digits very independently, and they obviously don't have an opposable thumb. But they make up for this lack of efficiency in their forepaws with another part of their body that is adapted to touch and detect objects.

These are the whiskers. Human whiskers are non-functional and are a vestige of evolution, but rats' whiskers serve an important function. Rats have five rows of whiskers, totaling to about thirty on both sides of their faces. The whisker arises from a special cell, which is quite like our hair follicles. But this cell is a receptor that is able to detect the qualities of the object the whisker touches. This cell then sends information to the brain; in much the same way as receptors on the palm of the hand sends information to the brain. These thin whiskers work amazingly like sensors.

Rats use whiskers to sense the world. They use them to hear, and they can judge between rough and smooth textures as well as human fingertips can. They are also able to judge distances (for instance, whether an opening is large enough for them to pass through), detect wind direction, balance themselves and perceive depth in small distances (in large distances, the eyes take over). They even use their whiskers for swimming. Rats depend on their whiskers to detect water currents and head position, and drown if their whiskers are clipped!

 ISBN 978-81-8477-736-9

If one looks more closely at the rat, one finds that the whiskers at the back (near the eye) are longer than the ones in the front (near the nostril). This is so because when the whiskers are moved forward and backward, which the rat does naturally, to explore, the whiskers stay the same length. Also, they serve different functions — the long ones at the back of the face near the eyes determine the location of an object and the smaller ones near the nose identify the object.

Just as we move our hands back and forth over objects, to detect textures better, the rat moves its whiskers rhythmically and touches objects with them to construct a three-dimensional image. A rat can extend its whiskers up to two inches in front of its head.

The movement of the whisker is important. The speed of movement is varied according to the need. Rats "whisk" faster when they are actively exploring a new object than when they are sitting quietly in a familiar place. They can also move individual whiskers. Sometimes, they can move two whiskers on the same side of the face in different directions!

Rats even use whiskers to defend themselves — they can fend off aggressive rats by maintaining whisker-to-whisker contact. If not, they are more likely to get mauled by the aggressive rat. A rat with its whisker clipped becomes "nervous", fights less, and even when it does fight, it is more likely to be bitten by an aggressor.

The whiskers in rats present such an efficient system that engineers are trying to build robotic systems that can identify 3D shapes based on the principles of rats' whiskers. In the future, robots with whiskers might be found exploring the surface of Mars or some dark, muddy, uninhabitable place!

Understanding the meaning

opposable
Mammals have **opposable** thumbs which are capable of moving and touching the other parts of the same hand.

vestige
A **vestige** is the remnant of something that no longer exists.

evolution
Evolution is a process by which organisms are believed to have developed from their earlier biological forms in the course of many centuries.

uninhabitable
A place is **uninhabitable** when it is not fit to live in.

 ISBN 978-81-8477-736-9

PRACTICE

A Match each word with the best meaning. Write the correct letter in each blank.

1 ____________ independently
2 ____________ perceive
3 ____________ rhythmically
4 ____________ exploring
5 ____________ aggressive

A moving in a pattern
B recognise or realise something
C separately, without help
D violent or forceful behaviour
E examining something

B Circle True or False for each question.

1 Rats in their lifetime cannot make up for their lack of forepaws with any other part of their body. Thus, they cannot touch and detect objects. (True / False)
2 Human whiskers are non-functional and are nothing but a mark of their evolution, but rats' whiskers serve important functions. (True / False)
3 If you want a rat to swim like a pro in water, all you have to do is clip its whiskers into half. (True / False)
4 Rats use whiskers to sense the world. The whiskers are used by them to hear, and also to judge between rough and smooth textures. (True / False)
5 Rats' whiskers are quite useful and act like sensors. However, when it comes to the task of defending oneself, rats have no use of their whiskers. (True / False)

C Read the text and answer the following questions.

1 Which part of a rat's body makes up for its efficiency in their forepaws?
2 How many whiskers in total does a rat have?
3 How do the whiskers help a rat to swim in water?
4 Can a rat move its whiskers independently?
5 How do rats defend themselves from other rats?

D Answer the following questions.

1 Why are engineers and scientists studying the functions of rats' whiskers?
2 Rats' whiskers work like sensors. Do you agree? Give reasons.

E Imagine human beings with long whiskers like a rat's! Using your imagination, write about what humans could do with their whiskers.

 ISBN 978-81-8477-736-9

3 Sting's Great Regret

By Sting

When I wake up next morning, I know there's something wrong. The light in the room is wrong. I feel wrong. I never sleep in; my father and his milk round cured me of that forever. When the sun rises, so do I. It is unthinkable that I would have slept in, but there is still something wrong. The noise in the street is wrong. This is not how the street sounds at seven in the morning. My eyes are now wide in terror, thinking the unthinkable. I turn my head slowly to find my wristwatch on the bedside table. I blink at it disbelievingly, shaking it in my hand, blinking at it again. It is five to one. My first thought is that it must be one in the morning, and then slowly, dawning logic presents the certainty, and full horror, of my predicament. I have slept for twelve hours, probably for the first time in my life, and I have almost certainly missed the birth of our child.

I leap from the bed and burst into Gerry's room. It is empty. I rush back, get dressed, and run upstairs to knock on Jim and Stef's door to use their phone (we still don't have one). There is no answer. Of course, they're working! I race to the phone box at the end of the street and feverishly call the hospital. My fingers can barely find the holes on the old-fashioned dial. The phone rings for an eternity.

Finally I get through.

"General Hospital, can I help you?"

"Yes, the Maternity Ward, please."

"Putting you through."

Another eternity.

"Maternity Ward." It is the Sister, the one who thinks all men are useless pests.

I take a deep breath. "It's me."

"And who might you be?" I can tell she knows exactly who it is, she just wants to play me like a fish on a hook.

"It's Frances' husband."

"Ah!" This now gives her full permission to torture me like

 ISBN 978-81-8477-736-9

an angler exhausting a heavy catch. There is a long silence as she lets out more line.

"And where might you have been, young man, while your wife has been labouring so?"

I can't take any more of this. "Sister, please, do we have the baby? Are they okay?"

"Yes!" I can feel the tug of the hook in my stupid mouth.

"Is it em — ?"

She does not allow me to finish the sentence, or take any initiative in this struggle at all. She answers abruptly, "You have a very healthy wife and son, and it's no thanks to you. Where were you?"

I ignore her question. "And Frances is okay?"

"She's fine!"

"Can I come and see them?"

"Visiting isn't till five thirty, you know that."

"Please, Sister!"

Now that she has landed me breathless and humiliated, she can afford some of her largesse. "Get over here right now!"

I race across town to the hospital, double park, and rush down the corridor, bursting through the double-swinging doors of the maternity ward like a saloon gunfighter, where I am greeted by the sight that is both joyous and also, leaves me slightly chagrined. My brother is in the centre of the room, holding the baby, grinning in his usual infuriating manner as if he's got one over me, firstly, because I'm half a day late and secondly, because my son looks exactly like him. I am in no mood for his innuendos, light-hearted or otherwise.

Thank God, Frances looks pleased to see me. My brother relinquishes the baby and we have a family moment.

"I'm so sorry. I don't know what happened. I slept in, and I never sleep in."

"Never mind. Look at your son; he has beautiful eyes."

In the years since then, I have tried to work out why a man who is never late for anything, and who rarely lies in bed after sunrise, would sleep in and miss one of the most important events of his life — the birth of his first child. I should have slept in the corridor. I shouldn't have listened when they told me nothing would happen and I should leave. The baby was born only a few hours later, at 1.30 a.m. If only we had a telephone.

 ISBN 978-81-8477-736-9

Understanding the meaning

feverishly
When someone acts in an agitated manner, he is said to be working **feverishly**.

largesse
When a person is being very generous, you are witnessing his **largesse**.

chagrined
When a person has been embarrassed or humiliated, he is **chagrined** or ashamed.

innuendo
A hint suggesting something, often sarcastically, is called an **innuendo**.

PRACTICE

A Match each word with the best meaning. Write the correct letter in each blank.

1 ______ unthinkable
2 ______ predicament
3 ______ logic
4 ______ useless
5 ______ humiliated

A disgraced or shamed
B of no worth
C too ridiculous to be considered
D a difficult situation
E something rational and reasonable

B Choose the best answer for each question.

1 Sting never sleeps in, he says. This is because
(a) his father's milk round cured him of that forever.
(b) of his father's and his habit of going for a walk every morning.
(c) his wife wakes him up on time every morning.
(d) his brother's pranks cured him of that forever.

2 Sting overslept for the first time, and
(a) missed his graduation ceremony.
(b) missed his brother's wedding.
(c) missed the birth of his first child.
(d) missed his daughter's dance recital.

 ISBN 978-81-8477-736-9

3 He knocks on Jim and Stef's door, but
   (a) they tell him to go away as they are working.
   (b) they are already in the hospital to meet his wife.
   (c) they are at work.
   (d) they have other plans, so they cannot help him.

4 Sting rushes to the hospital to find that
   (a) his wife is angry at him and doesn't want to see him.
   (b) his brother is already at the hospital, and is grinning in an infuriating manner.
   (c) his wife, brother and father have already left for home.
   (d) the nurse is still holding a grudge, and won't allow him to see his wife.

C Read the text and answer the following questions.

1 What makes Sting feel that there is something wrong?
2 This misfortune could have been avoided. How?
3 What does Sting compare himself to as he talks to the nurse?
4 Why does the nurse enjoy tormenting him?
5 Does Sting regret anything by the end of the story?

D Answer the following questions.

1 Describe the relationship between Sting and his brother?
2 What kind of a person do you think Frances is?

E Write at least 150 words about an incident where you have missed doing or attending something that was of utmost importance to you.

 ISBN 978-81-8477-736-9

4 How We Shrank the World

By Swagata Deb and Supriya Seshadri

Not so long ago, the world seemed very big. It was difficult to go from one part of the world to another. We did not know much about the people living in other countries and other continents. Even places that we think are pretty close today seemed very remote.

If a message had to be sent, it had to be sent with a messenger on horseback. If the place was far off, it would take days and weeks, if not months, for the message to reach. And in many cases, one could not be certain whether the message had reached or not. Today, if we want to send a message, we use a telephone or send an email. Such electronic messages are sent instantly. Also, we have trains, cars and ships and aeroplanes to take us from one place to another. Places do not seem so distant after all! How did all this happen?

In 1895—96, an Italian engineer, Guglielmo Marconi developed a method by which signals could be sent via air, without wires. These waves were called “radio waves”. Radio waves, first discovered by a scientist named Hertz, were used by Marconi to send messages. This marked the arrival of wireless technology. In 1876, Alexander Graham Bell invented the telephone, through which voices could be transmitted. Telegraph and telephone are methods of transmitting messages to distant places.

Reaching messages to many people at one time was done by what is known as radio broadcasting. In radio broadcasting, sound signals are converted to radio waves and this information is transmitted over large distances. Radio waves are directed towards the sky and they are reflected by the upper layers of the atmosphere (about 50—400km). These waves then reach far off places where they are received and converted into sound signals by what is known as radio receiver or simply radio.

 ISBN 978-81-8477-736-

Another important device used to transmit information to a large number of people at once is the television. The Scottish electrical engineer, John Baird, built the first television. His work was based on an invention of the Nipkow disc by Paul Nipkow of Germany. The Nipkow disc is a flat circular disc with holes arranged in a certain pattern. This disc is rotated to scan the object and the information about the object is converted into electrical signals. This kind of scanning is called "mechanical scanning". The television built by Baird was based on mechanical scanning. A new scanning was developed by Philo Farnswoth in 1930. He was the first to demonstrate a completely operational television that was totally electronic. The amazing thing is that he was only thirteen years old when he started working on it and he had a working model of a television when he was seventeen! Today, we have high definition colour television, and satellites are used to transmit signals to all parts of the world. Live television

 ISBN 978-81-8477-736-9

broadcasting has made it possible to know what is happening in any part of the world within seconds. The world has indeed become small!

Another very important concept that helped shrink the world is the Internet. Telephone lines are used to connect computers all around the world. This is called the World Wide Web. Through this, people can exchange messages by what is known as electronic mail or email, chat with each other and even have conferences with many people joining in at the same time. Pictures can also be sent at the same time, so that people can see each other while talking. The Internet has shrunk the world. The world is now small enough for businesses, hospitals and a host of other industries to collaborate effectively with each other around the globe.

Mobile phones have made it possible to get in touch with individuals everywhere in the world instantly. These are portable radios that send and receive radio signals. They are connected to a satellite network that makes it possible to access nearly any part of the world. Communication with anyone, anywhere in the world at the touch of a button is now leading to global awareness and a global consciousness. The whole world can now share the joys and sorrows of people anywhere in the world.

So far, we have been talking about connecting people in different parts of the world without actually going there. What about travel and face-to-face communication?

Man has been using rivers and seas for travelling since time immemorial. The early civilisations of Egypt and Greece used boats for trade and for war. They had a large number of oarsmen (100–200) to navigate the boats. As you can imagine, even though it was fairly high-tech for those days, it must have taken pretty long to move from one place to another by today's standards.

Till the twentieth century, the only way to cross the seas was with ships and boats. By the fifteenth and sixteenth centuries, European sailors had found sea routes that could take them to every corner of the world. Travel was still very slow and voyages to far off lands were still not easily accessible to the common man. Ocean passenger liners came in the early twentieth century. This made it possible for common people to travel to far off places; it took a very long time, many months in some cases, to reach their destination. The invention of powered flight (aeroplanes) completely changed the scene.

As the years went by, travelling across the ocean became easier and faster. Today, there are aeroplanes that can travel several times faster than sound. In 1976, a

 ISBN 978-81-8477-736-9

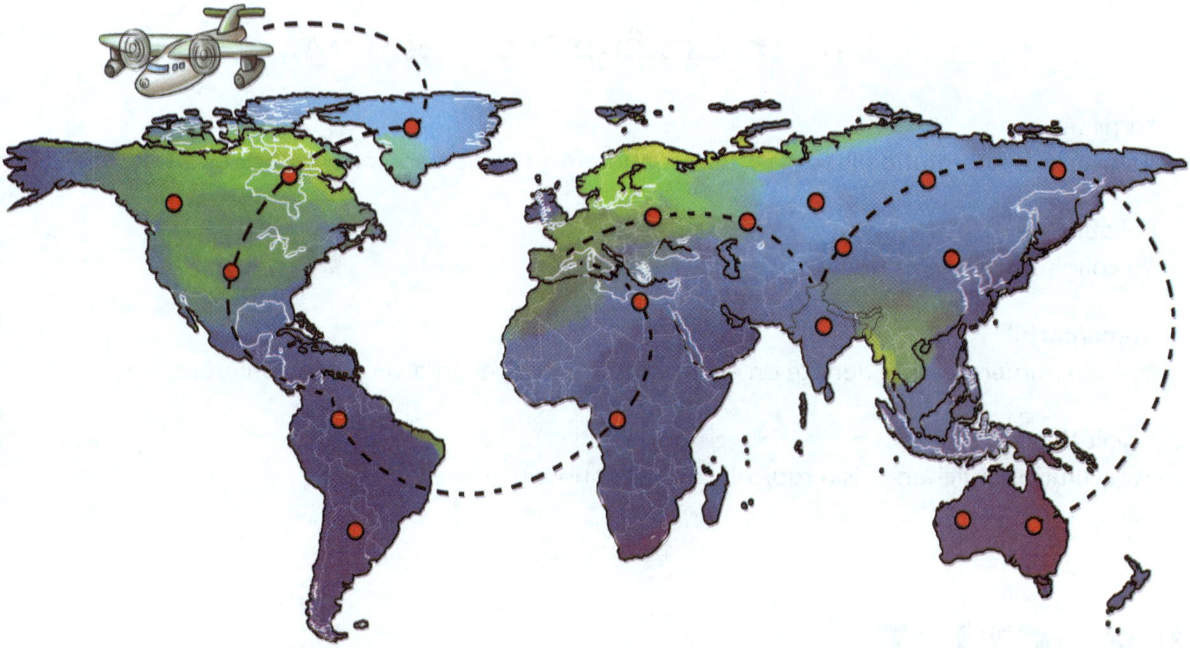

passenger aircraft called the Concorde was introduced, which could fly at a speed of about two times the speed of sound. It has since been discontinued.

In the meantime, transportation on land, too, was making a lot of progress. We all know that James Watt made revolutionary changes to the steam engine, which was used very effectively to work machines. From the transportation point of view, one important improvement made by James Watt was that he was able to link his steam engine to run a wheel. Then in the early 1800s, George Stephenson invented the Rocket, a locomotive which ran on steam power. It made a speed record by travelling at a speed of 47km/h! It made a speed record in those days! A very effective railway network was set up in the nineteenth century, which made it easier for people to travel from place to place on land.

From the mid to late 1800s, another type of engine was invented. This was called the internal combustion engine. This is the heart of cars you see on the roads today. The first car was built by Karl Benz in 1885, which is nothing like the cars we see today.

Today, we have a wide variety of transportation available to us: cars, buses, motorcycles, trains and aeroplanes. We can travel to the far corners of the earth with relative ease and comfort. The world has truly shrunk.

 ISBN 978-81-8477-736-9

Understanding the meaning

transmit
To **transmit** information is to pass information from one person or object to another.

collaborate
To **collaborate** is to jointly work on something.

immemorial
We use **immemorial** to denote an event that has happened a very, very long time ago.

revolutionary
A **revolutionary** change is a radically new or innovative one.

PRACTICE

A Find a word from the passage that means the same as each of these words.

isolated	__________	exhibit	__________
courier	__________	globe	__________
on air	__________	swap	__________
gadget	__________	consciousness	__________

B Circle True or False for each question.

1 Years ago when messages had to be sent to far off places, people made use of the Morse Code. (True / False)
2 In 1895—96, an Italian engineer, Guglielmo Marconi developed a method by which signals could be sent via water, without wires. (True / False)
3 The Nipkow disc is a flat circular disc with holes in a zigzag pattern. (True / False)
4 Mobile phones are portable radios that send and receive radio signals. (True / False)
5 In 1976, a passenger aircraft, Concorde, was introduced, which could fly about two times the speed of sound. (True / False)

 ISBN 978-81-8477-736-

C Read the text and answer the following questions.

1. How did people send messages to their near and dear ones in the olden days? How fast was this system of communication?
2. How did Guglielmo Marconi contribute in shrinking the world?
3. What is radio broadcasting?
4. What discovery is Philo Farnswoth known for?
5. Transportation on land made progress. In what ways?

D Answer the following questions.

1. Do you think technology has come very far in terms of travel and face-to-face communication?
2. If Marconi had not discovered radio waves, the world would not have shrunk. Do you agree? Give reasons for your answers.

E Imagine you are an inventor. Write in 150 words about any innovative technology or object that would help shrink the world further.

 ISBN 978-81-8477-736-9

5

The Mad Gardener's Song

By Lewis Carroll

He thought he saw an Elephant,
That practised on a fife:
He looked again, and found it was
A letter from his wife.
"At length I realise," he said,
"The bitterness of Life!"

He thought he saw a Buffalo
Upon the chimney-piece:
He looked again, and found it was
His Sister's Husband's Niece.
"Unless you leave this house," he said,
"I'll send for the Police!"

He thought he saw a Rattlesnake
That questioned him in Greek:
He looked again, and found it was
The Middle of Next Week.
"The one thing I regret," he said,
"Is that it cannot speak!"

 ISBN 978-81-8477-736

He thought he saw a Banker's Clerk
Descending from the bus:
He looked again, and found it was
A Hippopotamus.
"If this should stay to dine," he said,
"There won't be much for us!"

He thought he saw a Kangaroo
That worked a coffee-mill:
He looked again, and found it was
A Vegetable-Pill.
"Were I to swallow this," he said,
"I should be very ill!"

He thought he saw a Coach-and-Four
That stood beside his bed:
He looked again, and found it was
A Bear without a Head.
"Poor thing," he said, "poor silly thing!
It's waiting to be fed!"

He thought he saw an Albatross
That fluttered round the lamp:
He looked again, and found it was
A Penny Postage Stamp.
"You'd best be getting home," he said,
"The nights are very damp!"

 ISBN 978-81-8477-736-9

He thought he saw a Garden-Door
That opened with a key:
He looked again, and found it was
A Double Rule of Three:
"And all its mystery," he said,
"Is clear as day to me!"

He thought he saw an Argument
That proved he was the Pope:
He looked again, and found it was
A Bar of Mottled Soap.
"A fact so dread," he faintly said,
"Extinguishes all hope!"

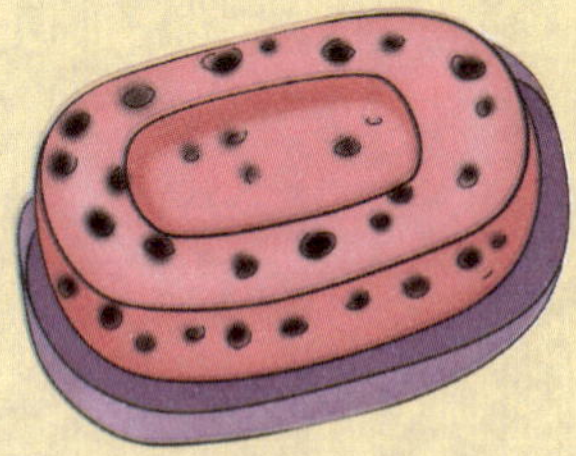

Understanding the meaning

fife
A **fife** is a small flute, usually used in military bands, that gives out a shrill sound.

mottled
An object is **mottled** if it has got patches of colour on it.

PRACTICE

A Match each word with the best meaning. Write the correct letter in each blank.

1 ____________ bitterness
2 ____________ practise
3 ____________ regret
4 ____________ descending
5 ____________ extinguish

A cease to exist
B to repent
C to apply
D resentment
E move in the downward direction

 ISBN 978-81-8477-736-9

B Choose the best answer for each question.

1 In the first stanza, the poet thought he saw
   (a) an elephant talking to his wife.
   (b) an elephant that practiced on a fife.
   (c) a letter from the elephant's wife.
   (d) an elephant on top of his chimney.

2 The poet figured out that the kangaroo working a coffee mill was:
   (a) a vitamin pill, if swallowed would make him healthy.
   (b) a hippopotamus, who if stayed to dine, would eat most of the food.
   (c) a vegetable pill, if swallowed, would make him very ill.
   (d) a hippopotamus working a coffee mill.

3 What was the bear without a head waiting for?
   (a) to be fed.
   (b) for his head.
   (c) for a bed.
   (d) for something to be said.

4 What did the author tell the penny postage stamp?
   (a) "How will you get home without a lamp?"
   (b) "You can't get home now, its best you camp."
   (c) "You best be getting home, the nights are very damp."
   (d) "You best stay here, the nights aren't very damp."

C Read the poem and answer the following questions.

1 What did the author tell his sister's husband's niece?
2 What did the author tell the penny postage stamp and why?
3 What did the author find when he saw a garden door that opened with a key?
4 What accordinq to the author extinguishes all hope?

D Answer the following questions.

1 Why was the author not happy to see the hippopotamus?
2 What do you think the author is really trying to say when he talks of the double rule of threes?

E Write in 150 words about an incident when you thought you saw something which turned out to be something else.

 ISBN 978-81-8477-736-9

6 Morozko – Father Frost

Retold by Aradhana Bisht

That year the winter was particularly severe. The ground was covered with snow. For miles around, there was a dazzling white blur that you could not look at without hurting the eyes. The sun barely came out, and if it did, it was only for a few short hours. Night fell swiftly and everyone huddled in their houses by the stoves.

It was on one such winter day that our story unfolds, in the house of a poor old man, his second wife, and their two daughters, one from a previous marriage. It was not a happy household. The wife was dissatisfied with everything. Her hard life had made her bitter and mean, and her only joy was her own daughter, Marfa, whom she pampered beyond reason. She would stroke her hair affectionately and exclaim, "What a clever girl you are, my darling. Such a beauty, my dear!"

As for her stepdaughter, Anastasia, she cared not a bit. She treated her like a servant and kept her busy all day running errands. Anastasia swept the house, fetched water, fed the cows. She was a good-natured girl and she did her chores without complaining. But no matter what she did, she could not please her stepmother. She could never be good enough. The old woman was ever ready with a sharp reprimand. "Not like this; that's no good! Go to bed without any dinner!"

Years passed in this manner and both the girls grew up. And on a bleak, miserable winter day, as Anastasia was doing her usual chores, she slid on frozen snow and dropped the pail of water she was carrying. Something snapped inside her stepmother. She screeched at her husband and said, "Take her, old man, somewhere far away. I cannot bear to hear or see her. Take her deep into the forest and leave her there."

There is an old Russian proverb: The wind will howl, rage and storm, and then it will stop. But there is no stopping a cantankerous old woman when she starts.

The old man begged his wife to change her mind, but she was adamant. Used to getting her way, she did not budge. "It is for her own good. Maybe Morozko will take her as his bride!" she cried.

The old man sadly brought out his sledge. "Come, my sweet child, get into the sledge," he said to his daughter.

 ISBN 978-81-8477-736-9

They travelled deep into the forest. There, on a snowdrift, under a huge spruce tree, he left her and quickly turned away so that he wouldn't see her freeze. He drove back home, tears blurring his vision. Anastasia sat on a pile of frozen snow, numb to the soul. She looked around her — every needle, leaf and branch hung heavy and white. Daylight was fading, turning a dismal grey; there was an air of anticipation in the air as though the forest was holding its breath till nightfall. Dreading darkness, Anastasia crossed herself and recited all the prayers she knew.

Suddenly, she heard a sound in the distance. Someone was approaching, crackling and snapping, leaping from tree to tree. It was Morozko. There he was, on top of the very tree beneath which she sat.

He appeared before her, a huge iridescent silhouette of a man. Anastasia felt a chill go down her spine. She steeled herself and sat upright. Then the figure spoke, its voice a silvery whisper, "Why, look who is here? Scared little girl, what are doing so far away from home? What brings you to my kingdom? I am, as you know, the ruby-nose-maker, Tsar Morozko. Are you a sinner or sinned upon by someone? But most of all, tell me, are you warm, my little dove?"

Anastasia could barely speak, with rasping breath, she said, "Greetings to you, Tsar Morozko, ruby-nose-maker. I am all right, thank you for asking."

As she spoke, the temperature dipped further.

"How goes the weather now? See my glory, do you like it?" asked Morozko again.

"Yes," she replied, awestruck by this force of nature, "It's beautiful."

Now darkness fell and Morozko gleamed even brighter. "Little girl, are you warm enough to withstand my chill?"

"Yes, I am warm," replied she, shrinking into a ball.

Morozko was pleased with the girl's answers, by her courage and respect in the face of nature's extreme grandeur. He wished to reward her. Suddenly, Anastasia found herself wearing the warmest, softest jacket she had ever seen. Blood coursed in her veins again, her breath became even, and she felt relieved. She sighed in contentment, "Thank you, beloved Morozko."

Morozko pointed a long icicle finger, and suddenly many boxes appeared. "What is this?" She gasped. Inside the boxes were — fur-trimmed fashionable coats, hats and gloves, pearl and diamond necklaces, bracelets and earrings, and a pair of high-heeled boots! The

 ISBN 978-81-8477-736-9

young girl had never seen such treasures before. She tried them on, a warm sense of joy filling her heart. Someone cared at last! Snuggling into her jacket, she fell asleep.

Next morning, the old woman hollered to her husband, "Fetch your daughter's body." But when he reached the forest, he saw her not dead but glowing.

As they reached home, the stepmother's smile froze when she saw Anastasia's radiant face. "What is this? Did you give her the riches?"

"She got them in the forest," he replied.

Greedy and envious, she ordered him to take Marfa to the forest. So, the old man went and left her at the exact spot.

Marfa had never left the house in uncertain weather. And being alone in a forest in winter did not please her. Her teeth chattered with the cold and she sniffed in her cosy fur coat. Daylight faded, and she hoped the ordeal would soon be over. Before long she would be home, in front of the stove, eating some delicious cookies and strutting around in her new clothes. Preoccupied as she was in her thoughts, she did not hear Morozko approaching, and was startled when the tree she was under swayed, spraying icicles at her. She was irritated. "What's that?"

"It is I," replied a hollow voice. "I am Tsar Morozko, the freezer-almighty. What brings you here?"

"It's of no concern to you, you old bones! Go away," she replied crossly.

The wind howled menacingly.

"You have quite a temper. Does it keep you warm?" enquired Morozko.

 ISBN 978-81-8477-736-9

"I am frozen, can't you see, you old croaker?" screeched the girl.

An ominous quiet descended.

Morozko came closer, "Are you warm?"

"I am frozen! Begone, you wretched Frost!"

Angry hail pelted Marfa, and her face turned blue.

When the day dawned, the woman hurried her husband. "Bring back my daughter adorned in gold and silver!"

The old man hurried and reached the tree, but was greeted with the unpleasant sight of a frozen Marfa. He took her body home.

His wife was at the gate, shouting, "Marfa, I have made your favourite dishes." She leaped onto the cart, and seeing Marfa's frozen body, fell off the cart. She went into a state of shock; never to speak again.

Anastasia married in the course of time, and often thought of Morozko. And when winter came, she enjoyed it and taught her children to respect nature.

 ISBN 978-81-8477-736-9

Understanding the meaning

severe
Severe is something that is very harsh or intense.

reprimand
To scold someone or disapprove of his actions is to **reprimand** him.

cantankerous
An ill-tempered or a rude person is a **cantankerous** person.

blur
Something that becomes foggy or unclear is a **blur**.

iridescent
Something that shimmers or gives off a brilliant glow of different colours when moved is **iridescent**.

contentment
A person has the feeling of **contentment** when he is happy and fulfilled.

ominous
An intuition that something unpleasant might occur is an **ominous** feeling.

PRACTICE

A Choose the word that has the closest meaning to the underlined words.

1 The old man's wife pampered her daughter, Marfa, beyond reason.
(a) indulge (b) treat
(c) show-off (d) cherish

2 Anastasia went about her chores, without a single complaint.
(a) disapproval (b) dissatisfaction
(c) objection (d) grievance

3 Morozko appeared before Anastasia, a huge iridescent silhouette of a man.
(a) portrait (b) description
(c) outline (d) body

4 He was pleased with her courage in the face of nature's extreme grandeur.
(a) dignity (b) glory
(c) state (d) brilliance

5 Anastasia steeled herself as Morozko appeared before her.
(a) prepared (b) organised
(c) encouraged (d) strengthened

 ISBN 978-81-8477-736-9

B Choose the best answer for each question.

1 The reason for the old man's wife's bitterness was
   (a) her want of jewels and riches which her husband couldn't provide.
   (b) her longing to stay young and beautiful forever.
   (c) her long and hard life.
   (d) her neighbours were rich and she was jealous of them.

2 One winter day, the old woman commanded her husband to
   (a) go to the forest and collect riches from Morozko.
   (b) take Anastasia and Marfa to the forest and leave them there.
   (c) get her beautiful fur coats and diamond necklaces.
   (d) leave Anastasia in the forest as she couldn't bear the sight of her any more.

3 An old Russian proverb is: The wind will howl, rage and storm, and then it will stop. But there is no stopping
   (a) a cantankerous old woman when she starts.
   (b) a man who has set his sight on his goal.
   (c) Morozko when he decides to test people.
   (d) a jealous wife when she demands things from her husband.

4 Morozko rewarded Anastasia by
   (a) giving her a boxful of the choicest sweets available in Russia.
   (b) naming a beautiful winter tree after her, and giving her his own ruby ring.
   (c) rescuing her from her jealous stepmother.
   (d) giving her a casket full of fur coats, gloves and precious jewels.

C Read the text and answer the following questions.

1 Do you think Anastasia's home was a happy household?
2 In your own words, explain the meaning of the Russian proverb given in the story.
3 Do you think Anastasia was a brave girl?
4 How did the old woman react when she saw the casket full of riches?
5 Explain Marfa's reaction and her attitude towards Morozko.

D Answer the following questions.

1 Give a character sketch of the old man's wife by analysing her relationship with her family members.
2 Do you think Morozko is a complicated character? Why?

E Write in 150 words, an alternate ending to the story.

 ISBN 978-81-8477-736-9

7 Houseful of Sparrows

By Ranjit Lal

We have all probably had sparrows nesting in our homes at some time or the other. They can be noisy and messy tenants. When I lived in Mumbai many years ago, a pair had built their nest on the top of the ceiling fan. I thought, what kind of parents are they going to be?

Just imagine: You're a sparrow fledgling, and have been raised comfortably in a flat in Mumbai. You've been well sheltered from the elements. Now, quivering with excitement and nervousness, you're ready for your first flight. Will you be able to make it, or will you crash ignominiously to the ground? You look down and your heart falls down a dark well. For, just inches below you, are three colossal steel blades whooshing very fast.

 ISBN 978-81-8477-736-9

You tell yourself — be calm. This is Mumbai, a city where the competition is cut-throat. There's a lot of pressure on your parents to ensure that you can take the toughest challenges. That must be why they've built their home there. They want you to fly through those deadly blades (equivalent of entrance tests of schools and colleges). If you succeed, you're ready for anything. And your parents have been flying through those blades too! But it's still a stupid place to build a nest. We had to dismantle it after one of the parent birds was killed by the fan.

Two sparrow families nest at either end of my balcony, and a few years ago, a war broke out between the two clans. I made notes. One of the females took a fancy to the handsome gentleman next door. With his black waistcoat and shiny chestnut plumage, he would strut around cockily. His wife did not approve of it. The two ladies went for each other. Both would cuddle up to the gent — one on either side — and hurl curses at each other. Alarmed, he would fly off into the nearby tree. His wife would follow, scolding him shrilly. The second lady would then vent her rage on the couple's nest. She would pull out the straw and scatter it. Tantrum-lady's husband too got into the act. He probably suspected that the gent next door had eyes on his wife. One morning, I found them on the balcony floor. They were facing each other chin-to-chin, glaring murderously at each other. They fought from 11.30 a.m. to 2.30 p.m. Their wives got involved too. There was a bleeding lady on the bougainvillea bush that evening. It must've been a draw because the hostilities continued for a week.

On another occasion, I was roused from slumber by a persistent cheeping inside my bedroom; a fledgling sparrow

 ISBN 978-81-8477-736-9

trying to walk through the closed door. It squatted in my palm looking woebegone. I placed it in a shoebox and put it in the balcony. Sadly, it died after two days.

House Sparrows are tough city birds and have adjusted to the bustle of cities. They are as noisy as big-city dwellers. They've settled all over the world — London, New York, Paris and Rome. They've never trusted humans, and whirr off at the slightest sign of trouble. They also construct untidy globular nests in trees. One pair has done so on a silver oak tree in the garden. This nest is right next door to the edifice of a pair of pariah kites, which means that kites do not always eat baby sparrows! In fact, the sparrows get protection from the kites, who don't tolerate cats near their tree.

Sparrows are basically seed-eaters. However, used to big-city life, they take on anything vegetarian. And even when they are calm, their hearts beat a thousand times a minute.

In recent years, there has been an alarming decline in the number of sparrows living in India and abroad. People in Delhi complain that they don't see these little birds in their gardens anymore. Some think that the new types of houses — all closed up, prevent sparrows from nesting. Another theory is that the exhaust from motor vehicles kills off the caterpillars which are fed to baby sparrows by their parents, so the fledglings starve. Whatever the reason, it will be a tragic day when sparrows disappear altogether.

On my holiday trips to the Himalayas, I have seen Cinnamon or Russet Sparrows, which appear to be gentler than the cheeky House Sparrows. Their plumage is caramel-coloured, and they fly in small groups, cling to stalks of wild grass and pick off the seeds. I think House Sparrows from big cities would regard them as being simpletons.

Ah, another quarrel has broken out in the balcony and I must see what it's all about.

 ISBN 978-81-8477-736-9

Understanding the meaning

tenant
Someone who lives in a rented house or property is called a **tenant.**

fledgling
A bird which has just developed wings for flying is a **fledgling.**

ignominiously
Ignominiously is a feeling that someone suffers when he is publicly embarrassed.

colossal
Something of enormous proportion is **colossal.**

dismantle
To **dismantle** an object is to take it apart or to disassemble it.

cockily
A person who acts **cockily** is someone who acts in an over-smart and cheeky way.

persistent
To be **persistent** is to be determined and firm in resolution.

woebegone
When a person looks depressed, he is **woebegone.**

PRACTICE

A Read the text and fill in the blanks with adjectives from the passage.

1 The author says sparrows are noisy and ____________________ tenants.

2 Sparrow fledglings of the city are ____________________ from elements.

3 On their first flight, fledglings would be ____________________.

4 Flying through ____________________ blades are like giving exams.

5 The handsome male gentleman sparrow would strut around ____________________.

B Choose the best answer for each question.

1 According to the author, sparrows can be
(a) our most faithful friends.
(b) brilliant neighbours.
(c) noisy and messy neighbours.
(d) annoying since they don't serve much purpose.

 ISBN 978-81-8477-736-9

2 The author compares the blades of the ceiling fan to
   (a) the parks and gardens in a busy modern city.
   (b) entrance tests of schools and colleges.
   (c) bigger predatory birds in the city.
   (d) the city people who do not care about nature.

3 A war broke out in the author's balcony because
   (a) a female sparrow took a liking to the handsome sparrow next door.
   (b) a kite also had a nest in the same balcony as the sparrow.
   (c) the sparrows didn't get along with each other.
   (d) the female sparrows couldn't see eye-to-eye.

4 Even when sparrows are calm
   (a) they like to harbour ill feeling towards other birds.
   (b) their hearts beat a thousand times per minute.
   (c) they run after kites in order to protect their nests.
   (d) they don't show it as it would make them seem weak.

C Read the text and answer the following questions.

1 Describe the feeling of a sparrow fledgling on the verge of its first flight.
2 What are the characteristics of the Cinnamon or Russet Sparrow?
3 What are the reasons for the decline of sparrows living in cities?
4 What characterstics distinguish House Sparrows from the rest.

D Answer the following questions.

1 What do you think the author is really trying to say when he talks of birds building nests and flying through blades?
2 Why do House Sparrows regard Cinnamon Sparrows as simpletons?

E Write in 150 words about an animal's living habits. Relate them to the lifestyle of the humans.

 ISBN 978-81-8477-736-9

8 The Little House

By J. M. Barrie

Foolish Tootles was standing like a conqueror over Wendy's body when the other boys sprang, armed, from their trees.

"You are too late," he cried proudly, "I have shot the Wendy. Peter will be so pleased with me."

Overhead Tinker Bell shouted, "Silly ass!" and darted into hiding. The others did not hear her. They had crowded round Wendy, and as they looked, a terrible silence fell upon the wood. If Wendy's heart had been beating, they would all have heard it.

Slightly was the first to speak. "This is no bird," he said in a scared voice. "I think it must be a lady."

"A lady?" said Tootles, trembling.

"And we have killed her," Nibs said hoarsely.

They all whipped off their caps.

"Now I see," Curly said; "Peter was bringing her to us." He threw himself sorrowfully on the ground.

"A lady to take care of us at last," said one of the twins, "and you have killed her."

They were sorry for Tootles, but sorrier for themselves.

Tootles' face was very white, but there was a dignity about him that had never been there before.

"I did it," he said, reflecting. "When ladies used to come to me in dreams, I said, 'Pretty mother, pretty mother.' But when at last she really came, I shot her."

He moved slowly away.

"Don't go," they called in pity.

"I must," he answered, shaking; "I am so afraid of Peter."

It was at this tragic moment that they heard a sound which made the heart of every one of them rise to his mouth. They heard Peter crow.

"Peter!" they cried, for it was always thus that he signaled his return.

"Hide her," they whispered, and gathered hastily around Wendy. But Tootles stood aloof.

Again came that ringing crow, and Peter dropped in front of them. "Greetings boys,"

 ISBN 978-81-8477-736-9

he cried, and mechanically they saluted, and then again was silence.

He frowned.

"I am back," he said hotly, "why do you not cheer?"

They opened their mouths, but the cheers would not come. He overlooked it in haste to tell the glorious tidings.

"Great news, boys," he cried, "I have brought at last a mother for you all."

Still no sound, except a little thud from Tootles as he dropped to his knees.

"Have you not seen her?" asked Peter, becoming troubled. "She flew this way."

"Ah me," one voice said, and another said, "Oh, mournful day."

Tootles rose. "Peter," he said quietly. "I will show her to you"; when the others would still have hidden her, he said, "Back, twins, let Peter see."

So they all stood back, and let him see, and after he had looked for a little time he did not know what to do next.

"She is dead," he said uncomfortably. "Perhaps she is frightened at being dead."

 ISBN 978-81-8477-736

He thought of hopping off in a comic sort of way till he was out of sight of her, and then never going near the spot any more. They would all have been glad to follow if he had done this.

But there was the arrow. He took it from her heart and faced his band.

"Whose arrow?" he demanded sternly.

"Mine, Peter," said Tootles on his knees.

"Oh, dastard hand," Peter said, and he raised the arrow to use it as a dagger.

Tootles did not flinch. He bared his breast. "Strike, Peter," he said firmly, "strike true."

Twice did Peter raise the arrow, and twice did his hand fall. "I cannot strike," he said with awe, "there is something that stays my hand."

All looked at him in wonder, save Nibs, who fortunately looked at Wendy.

"It is she," he cried, "the Wendy lady; see, her arm."

Wonderful to relate, Wendy had raised her arm. Nibs bent over her and listened reverently. "I think she said, 'Poor Tootles'," he whispered.

"She lives," Peter said briefly.

Slightly cried instantly, "The Wendy lady lives."

Then Peter knelt beside her and found his button. It was the one that she had put on a chain and wore around her neck.

"See," he said, "the arrow stuck against this. It saved her life."

Peter started begging Wendy to get better quickly, so that he could show her the mermaids. Of course, she could not answer yet; being still in a frightful faint; but from overheard came a wailing note.

"Listen to Tink," said Curly, "she is crying because Wendy lives."

Understanding the meaning

tidings
When someone gives you good news, he is giving you good **tidings**.

dastard
A person who lacks courage is a **dastard**.

reverently
Showing great respect towards someone is being **reverent**.

frightful
A horrible incident that shocks you, could be a **frightful** event.

 ISBN 978-81-8477-736-9

PRACTICE

A Match each word with the best meaning. Write the correct answer in each blank.

1 ____________ conqueror
2 ____________ dignity
3 ____________ tragic
4 ____________ uncomfortable
5 ____________ mournful

A feeling sadness and grief
B distress or sorrow
C unease or discomfort
D sense of pride and self-respect
E one who takes control of a place and its people

B Circle True or False for each question.

1 It was Curly who shot Wendy with an arrow. (True / False)
2 The boys were very happy, and rejoiced when they heard Peter's signal. (True / False)
3 Tootles was extremely sad and depressed about the whole situation regarding Wendy. (True / False)
4 By the end of the passage, Wendy passes away due to her wounds. (True / False)
5 When Peter tries to use the arrow on Tootles, Tootles tells him to go ahead and strike him. (True / False)

C Read the text and answer the following questions.

1 What misdeed had Tootles done?
2 How did the boys react upon seeing Wendy's body?
3 Thinking of Peter's reaction to Wendy's death, what do the boys think of doing?
4 For what purpose did Peter want to bring Wendy to the boys?
5 How did Wendy manage to survive?

D Answer the following questions.

1 In the light of Peter and the boys' reaction towards him, analyse and write about Peter's character.
2 Tootles was a brave boy with a lot of dignity. Explain how.

E Imagine yourself as Tootles. Write a diary entry about the whole situation from your point of view.

 ISBN 978-81-8477-736-

9 Mad and Madder

By Shirshendu Mukhopadhyay • Translated by Abhijit Gupta

It was late in the night. The situation was very tense in Manoj's house.

It all began with the arrival of *daroga* Nishikanta with a posse of constables. Nishikanta was a very strict *daroga.* Once, his two sons had fought with each other; he had sent them to jail for two days. On another occasion, his wife had gone back to her parents' house in a huff and he had issued an arrest warrant for her. He was strict with himself too. If he failed to catch a thief, he would run his nose on the ground, or tell one of his constables, "Give me ten strokes with the cane." He was also devoted to the goddess Kali. If anyone sang in praise of her, he would get a fit, roll on the ground, foaming at the mouth.

Everyone was in awe of Nishi *daroga.*

That evening, he stood outside the house and bellowed, "Bhaja-babu, the house is surrounded, don't try to fire your gun. If you fire, we'll fire back. If you run, we'll also run — I mean, we'll run after you."

Despite his strictness, Nishikanta was rumoured to be very timid. He took no kickbacks, but also could not kick back when required. He had little liking for firearms, and was not enthusiastic about arresting dangerous criminals.

Everyone from the house rushed out on hearing the commotion.

ISBN 978-81-8477-736-9

Dukkha-babu was teaching Manoj, Saroj and Putul. Ganesh-babu was engrossed in a song he had begun. On hearing the loud voices, Dukkha-babu said to the children, "Let's go indoors. It's a bit warm here."

Ganesh-babu's singing went off-key. On hearing the police, he quickly stepped out with his tanpura, intending to flee. But the moment he stepped out, a beam of torchlight shone straight in his face. Nishi *daroga* roared, "Drop your gun. Raise your hands."

Ganesh-babu said in a tiny voice, "Not gun, tanpura."

"Drop the tanpura then."

At this point, Rakho-babu came out, "What's going on here?"

Nishikanta said, "I have a warrant for your brother, Bhajahari."

"Warrant?"

Nishikanta wiped the sweat off his forehead, even though it was winter. "Don't pretend you don't know anything. You have been harbouring a murderer. Please take his pistol away, tie his hands and produce him before me."

"Whose pistol? Who's a murderer?"

Nishikanta smiled, "Why put on this act? If only I had known that Bhaja-babu was such a noted murderer! And under the guise of respectability lurked such a killer? Bhaja-babu's game is up. Bring him to me. And mind that he doesn't have his gun with him."

Rakho-babu gaped in astonishment. "Bhaju, a murderer?"

Thakurjee said from behind, "This *daroga* is possessed."

Thakurma cried, "Guns? He doesn't even cut bamboo for fear that he will hurt it."

Quite a few neighbours had come out on hearing the uproar.

Nishikanta said, "The real criminal can never be recognised from the outside. According to the principles of criminology, they behave like harmless people. Their criminal instincts are hidden. Therefore, Bhaja-babu is not as innocent as you all think. Nearly a dozen people in town have been his victims tonight. All of them had narrow escapes. He even made one of my constables do ten sit-ups. He nearly killed Harashankar the milkman, who saved himself by pleading for his life. He fired a gun inside the European Club, left Gobinda-babu and Shardul-babu half-dead, then went to search for his next victim. All these people have lodged complaints against him."

Ramu had been sleeping on the veranda all this while. On hearing the shouting, he said, "Bhaja-babu went out in the evening with his pistol. He was saying, he will teach all the goondas a lesson."

 ISBN 978-81-8477-736-9

Rakho-babu snapped, "Why didn't you say this before?"

"I wanted to, but Harashankar gave me such a blow that I was feeling ill."

The *daroga* said, "Rakho-babu, is this Ramu?"

"Yes."

"There is a complaint of buffalo theft against him. He stole a milk-yielding buffalo belonging to Harashankar. Arrest him."

Ramu began to yell, "In the name of Lord Hanuman, I never stole nothing."

Nishikanta turned to Rakho-babu, "You say that Bhaja is not in the house?"

"You can search the house," replied Rakho-babu.

"We'll have to. If he has not returned, I fear he has or is killing more people as we speak."

Thakurma wailed, "He can't even kill mosquitoes!"

Thakurjee said in a firm voice, "Look here *daroga*, you can't wear shoes inside the house while searching. There is no way I'm going to spray dung-water at this time of the night."

 ISBN 978-81-8477-736-9

Understanding the meaning

commotion
When there is a state of confusion and disturbance, **commotion** rules.

bellow
Bellow is a shout similiar to a loud roar.

engrossed
To be **engrossed** in something is to devote your full attention to it.

tanpura
A **tanpura** is a musical instrument which has four strings.

harbouring
To give shelter to someone or something, usually illegally, is **harbouring** it.

criminology
Criminology is the scientific study of crime and criminals.

PRACTICE

A Choose the word that has the closest meaning to the underlined word.

1 Nishikanta arrived at Manoj's house with a <u>posse</u> of constables.
   (a) gang   (b) armed men
   (c) mob   (d) search party

2 Nishikanta would <u>foam</u> at the mouth, and roll on the ground.
   (a) froth   (b) bubble
   (c) lather   (d) surf

3 Rakho-babu gaped in <u>astonishment</u>.
   (a) shock   (b) amazement
   (c) wonder   (d) excitement

4 Quite a few neighbours had come out after hearing the <u>uproar</u>.
   (a) riot   (b) disturbance
   (c) demonstration   (d) annoyance

5 Thakurjee said, "This *daroga* is <u>possessed</u>."
   (a) haunted by a spirit   (b) crazy
   (c) infatuated   (d) controlled by a spirit

 ISBN 978-81-8477-736-9

B Choose the best answer for each question.

1 The situation was very tense in Manoj's house because
   (a) *Daroga* Nishikanta had come over and was going to arrest them all.
   (b) Nishikanta had come to arrest Manoj, Saroj and Putul, on the complaint of an ice-cream vendor, who had accused them of stealing from him.
   (c) Ganesh-babu's off-key singing was disturbing the neighbours.
   (d) *Daroga* Nishikanta and his constables had surrounded the house, and had the arrest warrant for Bhaja-babu.

2 Nishikanta was a very strict *daroga*. He had
   (a) caught many dangerous dacoits in his career.
   (b) not spared even the senior official's relatives when it came to justice.
   (c) arrested his own sons and issued an arrest warrant for his wife.
   (d) locked even himself up in jail when he failed to catch a burglar.

3 On hearing the commotion, Ganesh-babu
   (a) got scared and tried to run away carrying his heavy tanpura.
   (b) confronted Nishikanta and told him to leave the premises.
   (c) tried to flee, since it was he who was the real culprit.
   (d) got hold of Bhaja-babu and handed him to the police.

4 According to the principles of criminology, real criminals
   (a) try to avoid large gathering since they are loners.
   (b) behave like harmless, regular people as their instincts are hidden.
   (c) give tell-tale signs as they have guilt written all over their faces.
   (d) are harmless people, who are in actuality, misunderstood.

C Read the text and answer the following questions.

1 Why according to Nishikanta, Bhaja was not what he seemed?
2 What were Bhaja-babu's real intentions?
3 On what charges did the *daroga* arrest Ramu?
4 What reasons did Thakurma and Thakurjee give in defence of Bhaja?
5 Why was Nishikanta a timid man?

D Answer the following questions.

1 *Daroga* Nishikanta was a man of contradictions. Do you agree?
2 Do you think Bhaja-babu is really a criminal? Give reasons.

E In 150 words, write a humorous character sketch of a person you know.

 ISBN 978-81-8477-736-9

10 Ancient Myths

By Cyril Birch

One day, the goddess Nü-kua, whose body was that of a dragon but whose head was of human form, grew weary of the loneliness of earth. After long thought, she stooped and took from the ground a lump of clay. From this, she fashioned with her dragon claws a tiny creature. The head she shaped after the pattern of her own, but to the body she gave two arms and two legs. She set the little thing back on the ground and the first human being came to life. They danced and made sounds of joy to delight the eyes and ears of the goddess. Quickly, she made many more of these charming humans and felt lonely no longer as they danced together all about her.

Then, as she rested a while from her task and watched the sons and daughters of her own creation go off together across the earth, a new thought came to her. What would become of the world when all the humans she had made grew old and died? They were fine beings, well fitted to rule over the beasts of the earth; but they would not live forever. To fill the earth with humans, then when these had gone to make more to take their place, this could mean an endless talk for the goddess. And so to solve this problem, Nü-kua brought together man and woman and taught them the ways of marriage. Now they would create for themselves their own sons and daughters, and these in turn, could continue to people the earth throughout time.

 ISBN 978-81-8477-736-9

After this gift of marriage from Nü-kua, further blessings came to man from her husband, the great god Fu-hsi. He too had a human head, but the body of a dragon. He taught men how to weave ropes to make nets for fishing, and he made the lute from which men first drew music. His also gave them the priceless gift of fire. Men had seen and feared the fire which was struck from the forest trees by the passing of the Lord of the Thunderstorm. But Fu-hsi, who was the son of this same lord, taught men to drill wood against wood and make fire for their own use, for warmth and cooking.

Already the creatures of Nü-kua's making could speak their thoughts to one another, but Fu-hsi now drew for them the eight most precious symbols with which they could begin to make records for those who were to come after. He drew three strokes to represent Heaven; the three strokes broken to represent earth. That symbol whose middle stroke was solid represented water, that whose middle stroke was broken represented fire. A solid stroke above gave the sign for mountains, a solid stroke beneath the sign for storm; a broken line below showed wind, a broken line on top showed marshland. With these eight powerful symbols, man could begin to record all he observed of the world about him.

For long years, men lived their lives in a world at peace. Then, suddenly, there spread from heaven to earth, a conflict that threatened to put an end to all creation. This was the battle between the Sprit of Water, Kung-kung, and the Spirit of Fire, Chu-jung. Down to earth came the turbulent, willful Kung-kung to whip up huge waves on river and lake and lead his scaly hordes against his arch-enemy, Fire. Chu-jung fought back with tongues of flame and scorching breath and halted the rebel Water in his path. Kun-kung struck his head against the mountain Pu-chou-shan, which was none other than the pillar in the western corner held up the sky.

Kung-kung made good his escape, but he left the world in a disastrous state. Great holes appeared in the sky, whilst the earth tilted to the west. In that region, deep cracks and fissures appeared which are still there to this day. All the rivers and lakes spilled out their waters, which ran off to the south-east, where the earth had slipped down low. They ran off to form a vast ocean there. Meanwhile, out of the shaken mountain forests, fire still raged forth, and wild beasts of every kind left their lairs to maraud through the world of helpless, terrified men.

 ISBN 978-81-8477-736-9

It was left to the goddess Nü-kua to bring back order to the world, to quell the fire and flood and tame the wandering beasts. It was she who selected from the beds of river stones of the most perfect colouring. These, she heated until they could be moulded, then with these stones, block-by-block, she patched the holes in the sky. Lastly, she killed a giant turtle, and cut off its powerful legs to make pillars between which the sky is firmly held over the earth, never again to fall.

So, the peace of the world was restored. But the mountains still rise in the west, and it is there that the sun, moon, and stars still run down the tilted sky; whilst to the east, the waters of the earth still gather into the restless ocean.

Understanding the meaning

endless
Something that has no end and keeps going on is called **endless**.

priceless
An object whose value is too precious to be even counted is **priceless**.

scorching
Scorching means intense or severe. It is mostly used to describe heat.

maraud
To **maraud** is to steal or plunder.

PRACTICE

A Fill in the blanks with adjectives from the story.

1 Goddess Nü-kua grew ____________________.

2 The gift of fire from Fu-hsi was a ____________________ treasure.

3 Fu-hsi taught man eight most ____________________ symbols.

4 To restore earth, Nü-kua killed a ____________________ turtle.

5 Even after restoration, the waters still gather into a ____________________ ocean.

 ISBN 978-81-8477-736-9

B Choose the best answer for each of the following questions.

1 Goddess Nü-kua's body was
   (a) a combination of human and dragon.
   (b) a combination of human and snake.
   (c) a combination of human and tortoise.
   (d) a combination of human and lion.

2 One day, Nü-kua grew tired of being lonely
   (a) so she came down to earth and made friends among humans.
   (b) so she made human figurines to keep her company.
   (c) so she told her husband Fu-hsi to make her another earthly kingdom.
   (d) so she took a lump of clay and made dragons to walk the earth.

3 Fu-hsi drew eight precious symbols. With these symbols
   (a) man could rule the beasts and control nature.
   (b) man could make fire and control water.
   (c) man could record all that he observed in the world.
   (d) man could, in turn, make their own little creatures to keep him company.

4 To restore earth, Nü-kua
   (a) patched holes in the sky, and cut off a turtle's leg to make pillars for the sky.
   (b) banished Kung-kung and Chu-jung from earth forever.
   (c) patched the holes in the ecosystem, and cut off a dragon's legs to stabilise the earth.
   (d) took lumps of clay and made more humans so that she could have more help.

C Read the text and answer the following question.

1 How did Nü-kua cure her loneliness?
2 What thought worried Nü-kua after she had made her first set of humans?
3 What blessings did human beings get from Fu-hsi?
4 What were the eight most precious symbols that Fu-hsi taught man?
5 What happened after Kung-kung made his escape?

D Answer the following questions.

1 What does the story tell us about Nü-kua's personality?
2 Do you think there is a deeper meaning to this myth? Give reasons.

E Have you heard of any other myth about the creation of life on Earth? Write 150 words on one if you have. Or use your own imagination and write how you think humans came to inhabit Earth.

 ISBN 978-81-8477-736-9

11
The Banyan Tree

By Rabindranath Tagore

O you shaggy-headed banyan tree standing on the bank of the pond,
have you forgotten the little child, like the birds that have
nested in your branches and left you?
Do you not remember how he sat at the window and wondered at
the tangle of your roots and plunged underground?

 ISBN 978-81-8477-736

The women would come to fill their jars in the pond, and your huge black shadow would wriggle on the water like sleep struggling to wake up.

Sunlight danced on the ripples like restless tiny shuttles weaving golden tapestry.
Two ducks swam by the weedy margin above their shadows, and the child would sit still and think.
He longed to be the wind and blow through your resting branches, to be your shadow and lengthen with the day on the water, to be a bird and perch on your topmost twig, and to float like those ducks among the weeds and shadows.

Understanding the meaning

nested
An animal is said to be **nesting** when it has made a home somewhere or taken shelter somewhere.

ripple
A movement or current in a water body is called a **ripple**.

PRACTICE

A Find a word in the poem that means the same as each of these words.

marvel	________	drapery	________
twisted	________	pined	________
descent	________	sit	________
fidgety	________	cover	________

 ISBN 978-81-8477-736-9

B Choose the best answer for each question.

1 The poet writes about a shaggy-headed banyan tree
  (a) standing on the banks of a pond.
  (b) standing tall in a beautiful clearing.
  (c) standing in the middle of a rustic village.
  (d) in the middle of a thriving forest.

2 The poet asks the great tree if he has forgotten about
  (a) the women who would come to fill their jars in the pond.
  (b) the animals who would take shelter under its shade.
  (c) the little birds who would perch on its branches.
  (d) the little boy who sat in its shade, wondering about the tree.

3 Who, according to the poet, has forgotten the tree?
  (a) the birds who used to nest in its branches.
  (b) the little boy who used to sit on its branches.
  (c) the ducks that swam by under the tree's shade.
  (d) the women from the nearby village.

4 Tagore says the boy wanted to be
  (a) one of the ducks so that he could swim under the tree's shade.
  (b) the wind, and blow through the Banyan tree's branches.
  (c) a bird, who would build a nest on the tree's mighty branches.
  (d) a Banyan tree by the banks of a pond.

C Read the text and answer the following questions.

1 Who is the poet comparing the child to?
2 What imagery of the banyan tree is the poet trying to evoke in the mind?
3 What did the boy do resting under the shadow of the mighty tree?
4 Who did the boy imagine himself to be?
5 Who all used to be there to give the boy company?

D Answer the following questions.

1 What is the poet trying to convey in the poem?
2 What is the importance of "innocence" and "childhood" in the poem?

E Research a well-known poet of your choice. Write at least 150 words about his or her life and works.

 ISBN 978-81-8477-736-9

12 In The Fog

By Arthur Conan Doyle

The night was clear and fine above us. The stars shone cold and bright, while a half-moon bathed the whole scene in a soft, uncertain light. Before us lay the dark bulk of the house, its serrated roof and bristling chimneys hard outlined against the silver-spangled sky. Broad bars of golden light from the lower windows stretched across the orchard and the moor. One of them was suddenly shut off. The servants had left the kitchen. There only remained the lamp in the dining room where the two men, the murderous host and the unconscious guest, still chatted over their cigars.

 ISBN 978-81-8477-736-9

Every minute, that white woolly plain which covered one-half of the moor was drifting closer and closer to the house. Already the first thin wisps of it were curling across the golden square of the lightened window. The farther wall of the orchard was already invisible, and the trees were standing out of a swirl of white vapour. As we watched it, the fog-wreaths came crawling round both corners of the house and rolled slowly into one dense bank on which the upper floor and the roof floated like a strange ship upon a shadowy sea. Holmes struck his hand passionately upon the rock in front of us and stamped his feet in his impatience.

"If he isn't out in a quarter of an hour, the path will be covered. In half an hour, we won't be able to see our hands in front of us."

"Shall we move farther back upon higher ground?"

"Yes, I think it would be as well."

So as the fog-bank flowed onward, we fell back before it until we were half a mile from the house, and still that dense white sea, with the moon silvering its upper edge, swept on.

"We are going too far," said Holmes. "We dare not take chance of his being overtaken before he can reach us. At all costs we must hold our ground where we are." He dropped on his knees and clapped his ear to the ground. "I think I can hear him coming."

A sound of quick steps broke the silence of the moor. Crouching among the stones we stared intently at the silver-tipped bank in front of us. The steps grew louder, and through the fog, as through a curtain, there stepped the man whom we were awaiting. He looked round him in surprise as he emerged into the clear, starlit night. Then he came swiftly along the path, passed close to where we lay, and went on up the long slope behind us.

As he walked he glanced continually over either shoulder, like a man who is ill at ease.

"Hist!" cried Holmes, and I heard the sharp click of a cocking pistol. "Look out! It's coming!"

 ISBN 978-81-8477-736-9

There was a thin, crisp, continuous patter from somewhere in the heart of that crawling bank. The cloud was within fifty yards of where we lay, and we glared at it, all three, uncertain what horror was about to break from the heart of it. I was at Holmes's elbow, and I glanced for an instant at his face. It was pale and exultant, his eyes shining brightly in the moonlight. But suddenly they started forward in a rigid, fixed stare, and his lips parted in amazement. At the same instant, Lestrade gave a yell of terror and threw himself face downward upon the ground. I sprang to my feet, my inert hand grasping my pistol, my mind paralysed by the dreadful shape which had sprung out upon us from the shadows of the fog. A hound it was, an enormous coal-black hound, but not such a hound as mortal eyes have even seen. Fire burst from its open mouth, its eyes glowed with a smouldering glare, its muzzle and hackles and dewlap were outlined in flickering flame. Never in the delirious dream of a disordered brain could anything more savage, more appalling, more hellish be conceived than the dark form and savage face which broke upon us out of the wall of fog.

With long bounds the huge black creature was leaping down the track, following hard upon the footsteps of our friend. So paralysed were we by the apparition that we allowed him to pass before we had recovered our nerve. Then Holmes and I both fired together, and the creature gave a hideous howl, which showed that one at least had hit him. He did not pause, however, but bounded onward. Far away on the path we saw Sir Henry looking back, his face white in the moonlight, his hands raised in horror, glaring helplessly at the frightful thing which was hunting him down.

But that cry of pain from the hound had blown all our fears to the winds. If he was vulnerable he was mortal, and if we could wound him we could kill him. Never have I seen a man run as Holmes ran that night. I am reckoned fleet of foot, but he outpaced me. In front of us as we flew up the track, we heard scream after scream from Sir Henry and the deep roar of the hound. I was in time to see the beast spring upon its victim, hurl him to the ground, and worry at his throat. But the next instant, Holmes emptied five barrels of his revolver into the creature's flank. With a last howl of agony and a vicious snap in the air, it rolled upon its back, four feet pawing furiously, and then fell limp upon its side. I stooped, panting, and pressed my pistol to the dreadful, shimmering head, but it was useless to press the trigger. The giant hound was dead.

 ISBN 978-81-8477-736-9

Sir Henry lay insensible where he had fallen. We tore away his collar, and Holmes breathed a prayer of gratitude when he saw that there was no sign of a wound and that the rescue had been in time. Already our friend's eyelids shivered, and he made a feeble effort to move. Lestrade thrust his brandy-flask.

"My God!" he whispered. "What was it? What in heaven's name, was it?"

"It's dead, whatever it is," said Holmes. "We've laid the family ghost once and forever."

In mere size and strength, it was a terrible creature which was lying before us. It was not a pure bloodhound and it was not a pure mastiff; but it appeared to be a combination of two—gaunt, savage, and as large as a small lioness.

Even now in the stillness of death, the huge jaws seemed to be dripping with a bluish flame and the small, deep-set, cruel eyes were ringed with fire. I placed my hand upon the glowing muzzle, and as I held them up, my own fingers smouldered and gleamed in the darkness.

"Phosphorous," I said.

"A cunning preparation of it," said Holmes sniffing at the dead animal. "There is no smell which might have interfered with his power of scent. We owe you a deep apology, Sir Henry, for having exposed you to this fright. I was prepared for a hound, but not for such a creature as this. And the fog gave us little time to receive him."

"You have saved my life."

 ISBN 978-81-8477-736-9

Understanding the meaning

serrated
An object is said to have a **serrated** edge if it's sharp and has a saw-like edge.

moor
A large peice of uncultivated land is a **moor**.

hideous
Something is described as **hideous** when it's extremely ugly to look at.

delirious
A person, who is in a disturbed state of mind and often hallucinates, is said to be **delirious**.

insensible
To feel **insensible** is to go numb or be devoid of feelling.

muzzle
The mouth and the nose, especially of an animal, is called a **muzzle**.

PRACTICE

A Choose the word that has the closest meaning to the underlined word.

1 Sherlock Holmes <u>stamped</u> his feet in impatience.
(a) trample (b) beat
(c) emboss (d) mark

2 There was a lamp in the room where the two men <u>chatted</u>.
(a) gossiped (b) laughed
(c) conversed (d) babbled

3 The man kept glancing <u>continually</u> over his shoulders.
(a) repeatedly (b) alternatively
(c) once in a while (d) generally

4 Holmes' face was <u>exultant</u>.
(a) sorrowful (b) puffed up
(c) elated (d) miserable

5 Sir Henry raised his hands <u>helplessly</u>.
(a) powerlessly (b) happily
(c) annoyingly (d) resentfully

 ISBN 978-81-8477-736-9

B Choose the best answer for each of the following questions.

1 Sherlock Holmes was getting impatient because
   (a) he wanted to kill the hound as soon as possible.
   (b) he wanted to talk to Sir Henry about important matters.
   (c) the fog was getting thicker and soon they wouldn't be able to see clearly.
   (d) he had a meeting with Lestrade and Sir Henry.

2 The narrator and Holmes pulled the trigger because
   (a) the hound was attacking Lestrade.
   (b) the hound was leaping towards them, howling.
   (c) the hound was hunting down Sir Henry.
   (d) the hound was trying to make its way towards the mansion.

3 When the narrator touched the hound's muzzle,
   (a) his hands got covered with blood.
   (b) his hands were slippery with sweat from fear.
   (c) he pulled back instantly fearing it was still alive.
   (d) his hands began to glow and smoulder.

4 When the hound went after Sir Henry, he
   (a) started crying in fear.
   (b) pushed the hound and fought him.
   (c) fell to the ground and was attacked by the hound.
   (d) started running towards Holmes and the narrator.

C Read the text and answer the following questions.

1 Why was the hound smouldering and glowing?
2 Who do you think the hound was after?
3 Why did Sherlock Holmes say "a cunning preparation"?
4 What was Holmes, Lestrade and the narrator doing in the moor at night?
5 Describe the hound.

D Answer the following questions.

1 After reading the passage, tell us about the character of Sherlock Holmes.
2 How did the characters in the story react when they saw the hound?

E Imagine yourself as the author of the above story. Write an alternative ending to the story in about 150 words.

 ISBN 978-81-8477-736-9

13 The Mystery of the Silk Umbrella

By Asha Nehemiah

Though they had lived in Chennai all their lives, this was the first time that Divya and Arjun had come to the temple tank. The scene around the temple tank was chaotic. There were shops wedged together, their goods spilling out onto the pavement.

"I can't see Pavamani, the umbrella repair man. He's usually around here, quite an unmistakable face."

"Unmistakable Pavamani's face might be, but I don't see how we can spot anyone here. I'm constantly being pushed."

"Just keep looking as you get pushed," Divya said.

Malli asked some vendors about Pavamani.

"I haven't seen him since last year. Someone told me he went on a pilgrimage and never came back!" the vegetable vendor said.

The man selling coconuts and camphor joined the conversation, "He got married and went to live with his in-laws in Goomidipoondi."

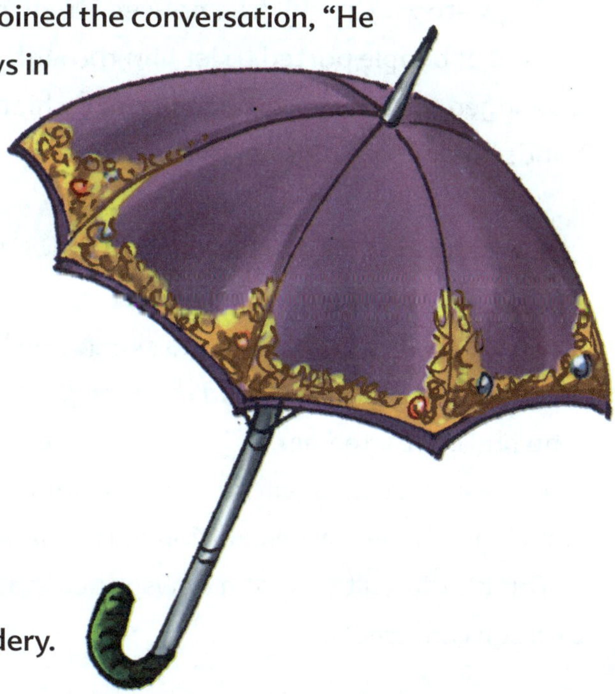

"Who on earth would marry him?" giggled the flower-seller hiding her face in her sari. "He looks like he has a piece of lime soaked in vinegar and tamarind juice in his mouth."

Roop Mani's umbrella attracted a lot of attention.

"Aha, aaaha!" exclaimed a pujari from one of the shrines. "That looks fit for a god," He stroked the silk and commented that he had not seen such fine gold embroidery.

 ISBN 978-81-8477-736-9

Cleverly, Malli left messages for the umbrella repair man.

"Tell him to come and see my grandmother. She has a marriage proposal for him," was the message left at Asokan Steel house.

"Tell him Ambujam Paati saw on her fortune-telling board that there's a lottery ticket he should buy," Malli told the owner of Ambika Appalam Depot.

After half an hour of fruitless searching, they took a break.

"I say give up and think of Plan B," said Arjun.

"You'll feel differently once you've had a few snacks. These are the best in town," Malli led them to a cart.

"Let's start with the chilli baji called "Silly Bajji" by our maestro," she indicated the man frying up large green chillies.

Malli ordered three plates. Divya looked uncertain; their mother did not allow them to eat from street vendors.

Arjun hissed, "It's fine. Freshly fried. Safe to eat!"

It was delicious. But before they could take their second bite, they heard a familiar voice calling out, "Stop! Stop!"

Divya and Arjun paused. That sounded like Shantha *athai.* What on earth could she be doing here?

"I say stop!" The children noticed a man running towards them. He was so fat that the sea of people parted to let him through. He jumped over a pile of pump accessories, zigzagged past the lungis and handkerchiefs displayed on the pavement and dodged the hands holding out plastic wind-up toys.

"Stop!" yelled Shantha ineffectually.

Desperation made the man run faster. Where on earth was the lady who was supposed to pick up the package from him? He didn't think he could evade Shantha Mani much longer. How on earth had she got on his track so quickly?

All he had to do was hand over the package he had stolen from Shantha to the lady who had contacted him. If he did that, he would be paid a sum which was more than what he earned in an entire year. The lady had said she would be at the temple tank, carrying a three-day-old edition of the *Financial Express.*

But it's difficult to spot a newspaper that's three days old when one is running through the streets.

 ISBN 978-81-8477-736-9

Malli sized up the situation, yelling, "Stop! Thief, thief!"

The single word galvanised everyone into action. From being passive spectators, the single word was like the gunshot that sets athletes running. The plump man found arms reaching out to grab him. He managed to extricate himself from the man selling sunglasses by giving him a shove. Running past the children proved to be his undoing. Malli put the umbrella out and tripped him.

The fat man lurched against Divya, who in turn slammed into Malli, sending the umbrella flying out of her hands. The fat man lost his balance, and sprawled awkwardly on top of the wooden platforms on which the flower-sellers had put flowers. The umbrella fell on the ground next to him, and was covered by the flowers knocked down from the platforms. The fat man stood up, dusting the flowers from his grey hair.

Shantha took a few moments to reach the spot. One of her slippers had broken. The chase had tossed her hair into a wild fizz.

"What nonsense is this? On what basis do you call me a thief?" The fat man was furious. He looked like a younger version of Santa Claus. He wore a shirt, and his baggy trousers were held up by a black belt above his paunch. He had curly hair and a curly grey beard which obscured most of his plump, pink face.

"Hand back my package, you villain!" Shantha demanded.

"Villain! How dare you? I am Dr Jones. Dr Bambaram Jones." He took his visiting card and handed it around. "I am the Director of Research at SOSO India. That's Seed Outreach for Sowing Optimisation. Look at my degrees! Double Masters from India and Germany, and Ph.D. from America."

One curious bystander took the card. "What did you say your name was? Here it says Dr B. Ambarnath Janardhanan."

"My colleagues could not pronounce my name when I was working abroad. So now, I'm known as Dr Bambaram Jones, or Bambi Jones."

"Hand my belongings," said Shantha.

"What belongings? Go on. Tell everyone what I took," he challenged.

"This man has stolen my ... my ... most precious ..."

"Most precious what?"

"He's stolen my precious antique ring! With a diamond as big as an elephant's teardrop!"

 ISBN 978-81-8477-736-9

The children were shocked. When Bambaram had collided with Malli and Divya, they had collapsed onto a shop selling nylon ropes, clothes hanger, and clothes' pegs. As they stood up, they'd become entangled in the metres of orange and green rope.

When Arjun tried to free them, they got more tangled. Shantha's statement made Divya and Arjun freeze. Their aunt hated wearing jewellery. They knew she didn't possess any ring or diamond the size of an elephant's teardrop.

"I have no ring." Bambaram turned his pockets inside out. He flicked open his wallet too.

Shantha didn't know what to do next. "I am going to complain to the cops."

"Complain by all means," Bambaram said dismissively as he bent to pick up the umbrella from under the flowers. He was going to get away with it!

The children didn't notice this, till Bambaram started walking away with the umbrella.

"Amma's umbrella! Give it back," Arjun shouted, but tripped over the rope lying in circles around his ankles, pulling the girls in all directions. Soon Malli and Divya landed on the floor.

 ISBN 978-81-8477-736-9

"Hey, that's ours!" Divya said.

Bambaram broke into a run.

The man was going to steal Amma's umbrella. But luck was on their side. Bambaram hadn't gone far, when he found several women blocking him. They were the flower-sellers whose flowers had been knocked to the ground when he had fallen. They demanded he pay up.

"It was not my fault. Those children tripped me."

"We don't care. It was your fat body which flattened the flowers. Pay us."

"Pay you? Such nonsense."

"We saw how much money you have in your wallet. You better pay us or else ..."

At that moment, a policeman appeared on the scene.

"What the ..." Bambaram was speechless.

"It's this man I called you about," one of the flower vendors spoke. "Try your excuses on my husband, mister," she said.

Made confident by the presence of the policeman, the vendors raised their demand.

Shantha wrestled the umbrella from Bambaram's hand, then hurried to rescue the children.

Bambaram was still arguing when Shantha and the children slipped away.

They paused near the juice stall to discuss what to do next.

"Go home," Malli said, "I'll take the umbrella to the shop. I'm sure Pavamani will come when he gets the messages. I'll have it repaired. It will be safe with me."

Shantha and the children went their way, and Malli started walking too. The entire proceedings had been watched by a slim lady carrying a tray of coconuts, flowers and camphor. She had grey hair, wore rimless spectacles, and was dressed in a white sari. She carried a newspaper which she tossed into the bin. She didn't need it any longer. After all, it was three days old.

 ISBN 978-81-8477-736-9

Understanding the meaning

pilgrimage
A **pilgrimage** is a journey that a person goes on which is of special importance to him or her.

dodge
To **dodge** someone or something is to move away quickly from their way.

galvanise
To **galvanise** is to shock someone into taking action about something.

PRACTICE

A Find a word in the passage that means the same as each of these words.

frenzied	______	covered	______
unsuccessfully	______	old	______
avoid	______	trampled	______
inactive	______	wordless	______

B Choose the best answer for each question.

1 According to the vegetable vendor, Pavamani was missing because
- (a) he had been kidnapped.
- (b) his in-laws were not allowing him to return from their place.
- (c) he had gone for a pilgrimage and never came back.
- (d) he had changed his profession and moved cities.

2 Roop Mani's umbrella, according to the pujari, was
- (a) fit for a king.
- (b) too old and tattered to be used.
- (c) too expensive to be carried around in a crowded marketplace.
- (d) fit for a god, given its fine embroidery.

 ISBN 978-81-8477-736-9

3 Divya looked uncertain about the prospect of eating Silly Bajji because
(a) her mother did not allow her to eat from street vendors.
(b) she had a sensitive stomach.
(c) the Silly Bajjis were being fried in unhygienic conditions.
(d) she wasn't really fond of fried food items.

4 Shantha accused Dr Bambaram Jones of stealing
(a) her precious antique ring with a diamond as big as an elephant's teardrop.
(b) Roop Mani's unique umbrella which had gold embroidery.
(c) her nephew and niece's plate of Silly Bajji.
(d) her copy of the *Financial Express.*

C Read the text and answer the following questions.

1 Why were Malli, Arjun and Divya looking for Pavamani?
2 According to his visiting card, who was Dr Bambaram Jones?
3 Who did Dr Bambaram Jones resemble?
4 By the end of the story, who takes the umbrella away and why?

D Answer the following questions.

1 Do you think Dr Bambaram Jones was what he said in his visiting card? Give reasons for your answers.
2 Shantha was as confident as Dr Bambaram Jones. Is this statement true or false? Give reasons.

E Imagine you were present at the market place at the time of the incident. In about 150 words, write your account of the tale.

 ISBN 978-81-8477-736-9

14 Three Men In A Boat

By Jerome K. Jerome

It seemed a fascinating idea. George gathered wood and made a fire, and Harris and I started to peel the potatoes. I should never have thought that peeling potatoes was such an undertaking. The job turned out to be the biggest thing of its kind that I had ever been in. We began cheerfully, but our light-heartedness was gone by the time the first potato was finished. The more we peeled, the more peel there seemed to be left on; by the time we had got all the peel off and all the eyes out, there was no potato left – at least none worth speaking of. George had a look at it – it was about the size of a peanut. He said: "That won't do! You're wasting them. You must scrape them."

 ISBN 978-81-8477-736-

So we scraped them, which was harder work than peeling. They are such an extraordinary shape, potatoes — all bumps and warts and hollows. We worked steadily for five-and-twenty minutes, and did four potatoes. Then we struck. We said we should require the rest of the evening for scraping ourselves.

It seemed difficult to believe that the potato-scrapings in which Harris and I stood half-smothered, could have come off four potatoes. It shows you what can be done with economy and care.

George said it was absurd to have only four potatoes in an Irish stew, so we washed half a dozen or so more, and about half a pack of peas. George stirred it all up, and then there seemed to be a lot of room to spare, so we overhauled both the hampers, and picked out all the odds and ends and the remnants, and added them to the stew. There were half a pork pie and a bit of cold boiled bacon left, and we put them in. Then George found half a tin of potted salmon, and he emptied that into the pot.

He said that was the advantage of Irish stew: you got rid of such a lot of things. I fished out a couple of eggs that had got cracked, and we put those in. George said they would thicken the gravy.

I forget the other ingredients, but I know nothing was wasted; and towards the end, Montmorency, who evinced great interest in the proceedings throughout, strolled away with an earnest and thoughtful air, reappearing afterwards, with a dead water-rat in his mouth, which he evidently wished to present as his contribution to the dinner; whether in a sarcastic spirit, or with a genuine desire to assist, I cannot say.

We had a discussion as to whether the rat should go in or not, Harris thought it would be all right, mixed up with the other things, and that every little helped; but George stood up for precedent. He said he had never heard of water-rats in Irish stew, and he would rather be on the safe side, and not try experiments.

Harris said: "If you never try a new thing, how can you tell what it's like? It's like men such as you that hamper the world's progress. Think of the man who first tried German sausage!"

It was a great success, that Irish stew. I don't think I ever enjoyed a meal more. There was something so fresh and piquant about it. One's plate gets so tired of the old hackneyed things: here was a dish with a new flavour, with a taste like nothing else on earth.

 ISBN 978-81-8477-736-9

And it was nourishing too. As George said, there was good stuff in it. The peas and potatoes might have been a bit softer, but we all had good teeth; and as for the gravy, it was a poem – a little too rich for a weak stomach, but nutritious.

We finished up with tea and cherry tart. Montmorency had a fight with the kettle, and came a poor second.

Throughout the trip, he had manifested great curiosity concerning the kettle. He would sit and watch it, as it boiled, with a puzzled expression, and would try and rouse it by growling at it. When it began to steam, he regarded it as a challenge and would want to fight it, only, at that precise moment, someone would always dash up and bear off his prey before he could get at it.

Understanding the meaning

precedent
An action that is seen as an example for others to follow is a **precedent**.

piquant
Generally when a dish is spicy or has a sharp taste, it is **piquant**.

precise
To be **precise** is to be exact or to the point.

PRACTICE

A Find a word in the passage that means the same as each of these words.

captivating	____________	sincere	____________
attempting	____________	healthy	____________
leftovers	____________	awaken	____________
exhibited	____________	contest	____________

 ISBN 978-81-8477-736

B Circle True or False for each question.

1 According to the narrator, peeling potatoes was like a walk in the park. (True / False)
2 The advantage of cooking Irish stew is that you can get rid of a lot of other leftover food items. (True / False)
3 For Harris, trying new things means a whole lot of time wasted, especially if you're running short of time. (True / False)
4 Montmorency was fond of the kettle because the boiling of water in it indicated that it was time for tea, and biscuit treats for him. (True / False)
5 The boys liked to watch Montmorency gear up for the challenge, and would let him tackle his prey. (True / False)

C Read the text and answer the following questions.

1 What was the "fascinating idea" that the narrator talks about?
2 What happened when the narrator started peeling potatoes for the first time?
3 What other ingredients did the boys add to the Irish stew?
4 What was the narrator's observation after he tasted the stew?
5 Who was Montmorency? What was his contribution towards the Irish stew?

D Answer the following questions.

1 There is an important lesson in the story. What is it and why is it important?
2 Do you see any difference in the personalities of George and Harris?

E What is your favourite dish? Write a detailed recipe for its preparation. You may create your own recipe.

 ISBN 978-81-8477-736-9

15 Success Is Counted Sweetest

By Emily Dickinson

Success is counted sweetest
By those who ne'er succeed.
To comprehend a nectar
Requires sorest need.

Not one of all the purple Host
Who took the Flag today
Can tell the definition
So clear of Victory

As he defeated — dying —
On whose forbidden ear
The distant strains of triumph
Burst agonised and clear!

 ISBN 978-81-8477-736-9

Understanding the meaning

ne'er
Ne'er is an old-English usage of the word "never".

strains
Strains can be used for the words, tension or noise.

PRACTICE

A Find words from the poem that have the same meaning as these words.

understand	____________	achievement	____________
severe	____________	prohibited	____________
description	____________	tormented	____________

B Circle True or False for each question.

1 Success is understood by only those who have always tasted the sweet fruits of victory. (True / False)
2 Emily Dickinson is trying to show the difficulties of attaining success by people who have not achieved anything in life. (True / False)
3 "Purple Host" evokes imagery of army and battlefield. (True / False)
4 Only when one has lost, can one truly appreciate success. (True / False)
5 The last stanza tells us that when you are defeated, all is lost. (True / False)

C Read the poem and answer the following questions.

1 To whom does success seem sweetest?
2 What does the poet mean by the word "nectar" in the poem?
3 Who, according to the poet, can tell the definition of "victory"?
4 What does "purple host" mean?
5 What does the word "triumph" signify?

D Answer the following questions.

1 Not everyone can appreciate success. Elaborate.
2 What is the irony in the last stanza?

E Write in 150 words, what success means to you and what importance it holds in your life.

 ISBN 978-81-8477-736-9

16 A Strange Visitor

By Robert Louis Stevenson

It was not very long that there occurred the first of the mysterious events. It was a bitter cold winter and it was plain from the first that my poor father was little likely to see the spring. He sank daily, and my mother and I had the inn upon our hands, and were kept busy enough without paying much regard to our unpleasant guest.

It was a January morning, the captain had risen earlier than usual and set out down the beach, his cutlass swinging under the old blue coat, his brass telescope under his arm, his hat tilted back. His breath was hanging like smoke , and the last sound I heard of him was a loud snort of indignation. I was laying the breakfast table when the parlour door opened and a man stepped in. He was a pale, tallow creature, wanting two fingers of the left hand, and though he wore a cutlass, he did not look much

 ISBN 978-81-8477-736-9

like a fighter. I had always my eye open for seafaring men, but this one puzzled me. He was not sailorly, yet he had a smack of the sea about him.

He sat down upon a table and motioned me to draw near. I paused where I was.

"Come here, sonny."

I took a step nearer.

"Is this here table for my mate Bill?" he asked with a kind of leer.

I told him I did not know his mate Bill, and this was for a person called the captain.

"My mate Bill would be called the Captain. He has a cut on one cheek and a mighty pleasant way with him, particularly in drink. For argument, your captain has a cut on one cheek – if you like, that cheek's the right one. Ah, well! I told you. Now, is my mate Bill here?"

I told him he was out walking.

"Which way, sonny?"

I pointed out the rock and told him when the captain was likely to return. "This'll be as good as drink to my mate Bill."

The expression of his face as he said these words was not at all pleasant. But it was no affair of mine, I thought. The stranger kept hanging about just inside the inn door, peering round the corner like a cat waiting for a mouse. Once I stepped out myself, but he immediately called me back, and as I did not obey quick enough, a most horrible change came over his tallowy face, and he ordered me in with an oath that made me jump. As soon as I was back again, he returned to his former manner and told me he had taken quite a fancy to me. "I have a son of my own – as like you as two blocks, and he's all the pride of my 'art. But the great thing for boys is discipline, sonny – discipline. Now, if you had sailed along of Bill, you wouldn't have stood there to be spoke to twice – not you. That was never Bill's way, nor the way of such as sailed with him. And here, sure enough, is my mate Bill, with a spy-glass under his arm. You and me'll just go back into the parlour, and get behind the door, and we'll give Bill a little surprise."

The stranger backed along with me into the parlour and put me behind him in the corner so that we were both hidden by the open door. I was very uneasy. It added to my fears to observe that he was frightened himself. He loosened the blade in the sheath; and all the time we were waiting there he kept swallowing.

 ISBN 978-81-8477-736-9

At last, in strode the captain, slammed the door behind him, without looking to the right or left, and marched straight across the room to where his breakfast awaited him.

"Bill," said the stranger in a voice that I thought he had tried to make bold and big.

The captain spun round on his heel; all the brown had gone out of his face, and even his nose was blue; he had the look of a man who sees a ghost, or the evil one, or something worse. I felt sorry to see him turn so old and sick.

"Come, Bill, you know me; you know an old shipmate," said the stranger.

The captain gasped.

"Black Dog!"

 ISBN 978-81-8477-736-9

"Black Dog as ever was, come for to see his old shipmate Billy, at the Admiral Benbow inn. Ah, Bill, Bill, we have seen a sight of times, us two, since I lost them two talons," holding up his mutilated hand.

"Now, look here," said the captain; "you've run me down; here I am; well, then, speak up; what is it?"

"That's you, Bill," returned Black Dog, "you're in the right of it, Billy. I'll have a glass of rum from this dear child here, as I've took such a liking to; and we'll sit down, if you please, and talk square, like old shipmates."

When I returned with the rum, they were already seated on either side of the captain's breakfast table — Black Dog next to the door and sitting sideways so as to have one eye on his old shipmate and one on his retreat.

He bade me go and leave the door wide open. "None of your keyholes for me, sonny," he said; and I left them together and retired into the bar.

For a long time, I did my best to listen, I could hear nothing; but at last the voices began to grow higher, and I could pick up a word or two, mostly oaths, from the captain.

"No, no, no, no; and an end of it!" he cried once. And again, "If it comes to swinging, swing all, say I."

Then, all of a sudden there was a tremendous noise — the chair and table went over in a lump, a clash of steel followed, and then a cry of pain, and the next instant I saw Black Dog in full flight, and the captain hotly pursuing, both with drawn cutlasses, and the former streaming blood from the left shoulder. Just at the door, the captain aimed at the fugitive one last tremendous cut, which would certainly have split him to the chine had it not been intercepted by our big signboard of Admiral Benbow. You may see the notch on the lower side of the frame to this day.

Once out upon the road, Black Dog, in spite of his wound, disappeared over the edge of the hill in half a minute. The captain, for his part, stood staring at the signboard like a bewildered man. Then he passed his hand over his eyes several times and at last turned back into the house.

"Jim," says he, "rum"; and as he spoke, he reeled a little, and caught himself with one hand against the wall.

"Are you hurt?" cried I.

"Rum," he repeated. "I must get away from here. Rum! Rum!"

 ISBN 978-81-8477-736-9

I ran to fetch it, but I was quite unsteadied, and I broke one glass and fouled the tap, and while I was still getting in my own way, I heard a loud fall in the parlour, and running in, beheld the captain lying full length upon the floor. At the same instant, my mother, alarmed by the cries and fighting, came running downstairs. Between us, we raised his head. He was breathing very loud and hard, but his eyes were closed and his face a horrible colour.

"Dear, deary me," cried my mother, "what a disgrace upon the house!"

We had no idea what to do to help the captain. I got the rum and tried to put it down his throat, but his teeth were tightly shut and his jaws as strong as iron. It was a happy relief for us when the door opened and Doctor Livesey came in, on his visit to my father.

"Oh, doctor," we cried, "what shall we do? Where is he wounded?"

"Wounded? A fiddle-stick's end!" said the doctor. "No more wounded than you or I. The man has had a stroke, as I warned him. Now, Mrs. Hawkins, just you run upstairs to your husband and tell him, if possible, nothing about it. For my part, I must do my best to save this fellow's trebly worthless life; Jim, you get me a basin."

When I got back with the basin, the doctor had already ripped up the captain's sleeve and exposed his great sinewy arm. It was tattooed in several places. "Here's luck," "A fair wind," and "Billy Bones his fancy," were very neatly and clearly executed on the forearm; and up near the shoulder, there was a sketch of a gallows and a man hanging from it.

"Prophetic," said the doctor, touching this picture with his finger. "And now, Master Billy Bones, if that be your name, we'll have a look at the colour of your blood. Jim," he said, "are you afraid of blood?"

"No, sir," said I.

"Well, then," said he, "you hold the basin"; and with that he took his lancet and opened a vein.

A great deal of blood was taken before the captain opened his eyes. First, he recognised the doctor with an unmistakable frown; then his glance fell upon me, and he looked relieved. But suddenly his colour changed, and he tried to raise himself, "Where's Black Dog?"

 ISBN 978-81-8477-736-9

"There is no Black Dog here," said the doctor, "except what you have on your own back. You have been drinking rum; you have had a stroke; and I have much against my own will, dragged you head foremost out of the grave."

"What I have to say to you is this: one glass of rum won't kill you, but if you take one, you'll take another and another, and I stake my wig if you don't break off short, you'll die — do you understand that? Come now, make an effort. I'll help you to your bed for once," continued the doctor.

We managed to hoist him upstairs, and laid him on his bed, where his head fell back on the pillow.

"Now, mind you," said the doctor. "The name of rum for you is death."

And with that he went off taking me with him by the arm.

"This is nothing," he said as he closed the door. "I have drawn blood enough to keep him quiet a while; he should lie for a week where he is —but another stroke would settle him."

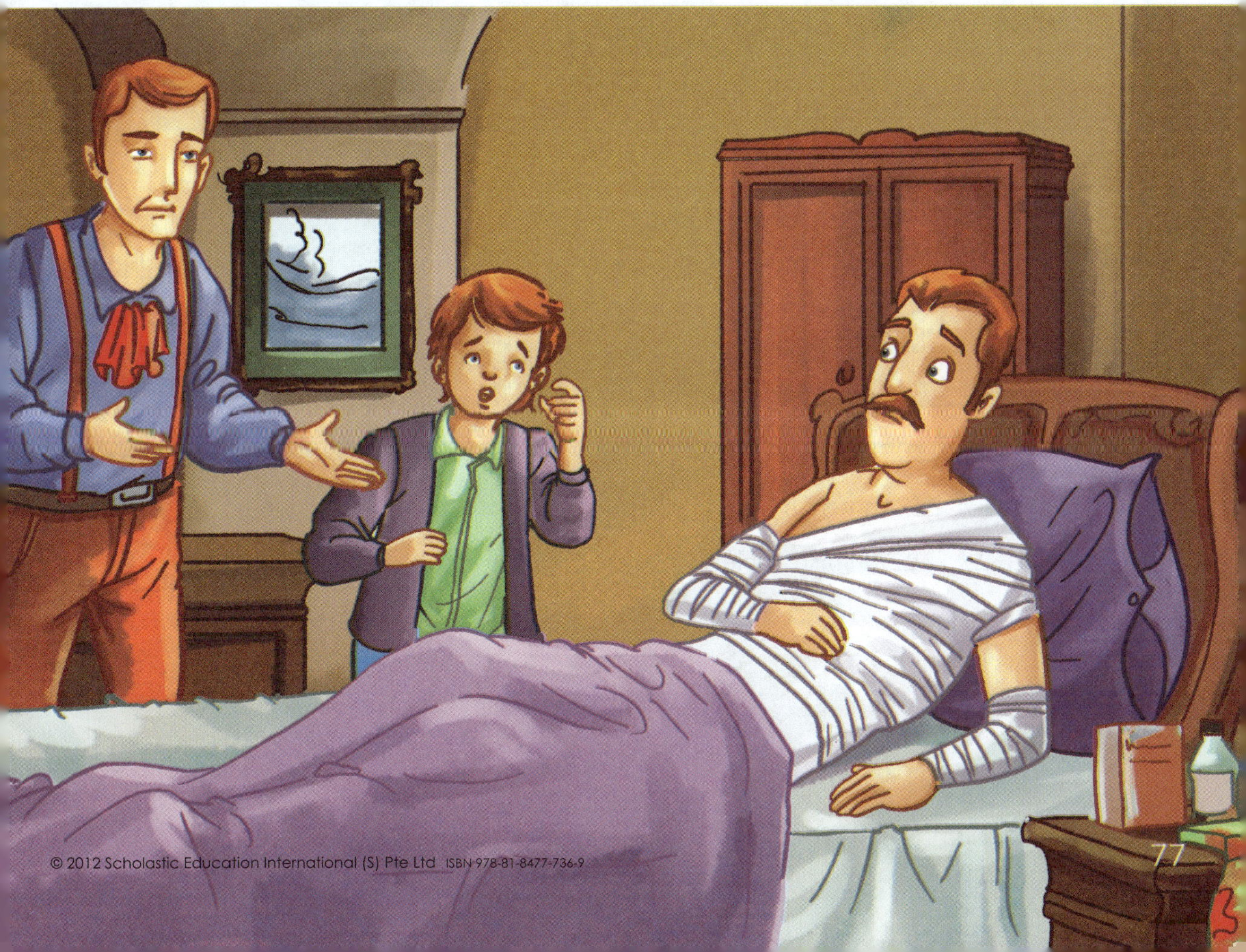

 ISBN 978-81-8477-736-9

Understanding the meaning

cutlass
A **cutlass** is a curvy, sharp and slightly short sword which was used by sailors in the olden days.

tallow
Tallow is used to refer to a hardy substance. Here it is used for the person's complexion.

indignation
Anger that is felt towards unjust treatment is **indignation**.

sheath
A **sheath** is a covering for a knife, blade or sword.

retreat
To go back or withdraw is to **retreat**.

fugitive
A man accused of a crime and on the run, is a **fugitive**.

mutilated
Something or someone is **mutilated** when they have suffered a serious injury that has disfigured them.

bewildered
When someone is in a state of confusion, he or she is **bewildered**.

lancet
A **lancet** is a surgical knife used by doctors during operations.

PRACTICE

A Match each word with the best meaning. Write the correct letter in each blank.

1 __________ mysterious
2 __________ sinewy
3 __________ intercept
4 __________ notch
5 __________ unmistakable

A A deep cut made on the surface of an object
B Something that is very distinctive or typical
C Something that is very tough to understand
D Someone who is muscular
E To obstruct something or someone

 ISBN 978-81-8477-736-9

B Choose the best answer for each question.

1 The narrator and his mother were left to care for the inn because
   (a) the narrator's father was in the army and was fighting in the war.
   (b) the narrator realised that he was old enough to be responsible.
   (c) the narrator's father was sick and was bedridden.
   (d) the narrator's father was good for nothing and used to gamble all the time.

2 The narrator was laying the breakfast table when
   (a) the door opened and in stepped a pale-looking man who was missing two fingers of the left hand. He wore a cutlass, but did not look like a fighter.
   (b) the door opened and in stepped the captain, screaming, "Where is the Black Dog?"
   (c) the door opened and in stepped a ferocious-looking man who was missing two fingers on both his hands. He wore an eye-patch and carried a cutlass.
   (d) the door opened and the Black Dog and the captain stumbled in, engaged in a fight.

3 The narrator was excused from the room, but he heard
   (a) the Black Dog and the captain having an argument about a certain treasure island.
   (b) the Black Dog and the captain singing about their glory days as pirates.
   (c) the Black Dog and the captain hatching a plan to invade an island which had buried gold.
   (d) loud voices and abusing which resulted in a fight between the two men.

4 Mrs Hawkins and the narrator were unsure what do to with the captain when
   (a) to their relief the door opened and Doctor Livesey came in, on his visit to his father.
   (b) to their shock the Black Dog was back, holding his cutlass, wanting to murder the captain.
   (c) the narrator's father stumbled into the room and demanded an explanation.
   (d) to their relief the door opened and Doctor Livesey came in, but so did the police.

C Read the text and answer the following questions.

1 What was the narrator's complaint about the weather?
2 Describe the Black Dog's personality and appearance.
3 What was the mother's concern when she saw the wounded captain?
4 What did Doctor Livesey say was wrong with the captain? What did he do afterwards?
5 What was Doctor Livesey's reaction upon seeing the captain's many tattoos?

 ISBN 978-81-8477-736-9

D Answer the following questions.

1 Do you think the narrator was an observant boy? Give reasons.
2 Doctor Livesey was a practical man. Do you agree?

E Write in 150 words about the character of the captain. Use your imagination to give a background to his life story.

 ISBN 978-81-8477-736-9